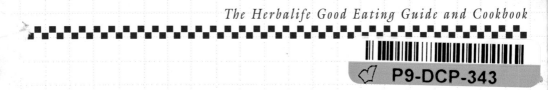
Dedication

To my husband David
with all my love and appreciation.

Printed in the United States of America
ISBN 0-9651736-0-7
Library of Congress Cataloging in Publication Data

PRIMO PARTY!

Buy any large Primo and get any additional pizza for $6 each (Limit 5)

Family Meal Deal
1 large primo pizza, 1 small cheese pizza,
2 sides of fries, 1 order of cheese breadsticks

ONLY $14⁹⁹

Offer on traditional thin crust pizza only.
VALID ON DINE-IN, CARRY-OUT OR DELIVERY (WHERE AVAILABLE)

One coupon accepted per item per visit or delivery. Call for delivery availability. Limited delivery area. Add $1 per delivery order, $7.50 delivery minimum. Not valid with other discounts or specials. Expires 12/31/98.

COUPON 7042

---

2 Large Cheese or Pepperoni Pizzas

ONLY $12⁹⁹

Offer on traditional thin crust pizza only.
VALID ON DINE-IN, CARRY-OUT OR DELIVERY (WHERE AVAILABLE)

One coupon accepted per item per visit or delivery. Call for delivery availability. Limited delivery area. Add $1 per delivery order, $7.50 delivery minimum. Not valid with other discounts or specials. Expires 12/31/98.
COUPON 7153 (2 Cheese), COUPON 7154 (2 Pepperoni)
COUPON 7155 (1 of Each)

Acknowledgements

I would like to thank Allegra Burton, M.S., R.D., for her valuable assistance with the preparation of the produce section of the book; Gale Rudolph, Ph.D., C.N.S., for her advice on food labeling and for her review of the recipes; Lisa Chang, M.P.H., for her superb editing and moral support; Nina Sokol, M.S., R.D., for her excellent checking of the recipes and nutritional information. This book would not have been possible without them and all of the staff of the Corporate Marketing Division at Herbalife. My thanks to them all.

The Herbalife Good Eating Guide and Cookbook

by CAROLYN KATZIN, M.S., C.N.S.

Your ONE Essential Guide To Healthy Eating Includes

Foreword by Mark Hughes, President and Founder

Introduction by David B. Katzin M.D., Ph.D.
Chairman of Herbalife's Medical Advisory Board

Herbalife's Good Nutrition Guide

How to Equip your Kitchen

How to Select the Freshest and Best Foods

Nutritional Value of Fruits, Vegetables, Culinary Herbs and Spices

Over 200 Delicious and Healthy Recipes including
Nutritional Information

Table of Contents

Foreword by Mark Hughes
Introduction by David B. Katzin, M.D., Ph.D.

Foreword

by Mark Hughes, President and Founder

As the Herbalife dream expands, more people than ever have a chance to lose weight while getting good nutrition. When I began Herbalife over 16 years ago, I wanted people to have an effective way to lose weight without damaging their health. Today Herbalife is in over 30 countries, and we have affected the lives of literally millions of people. As Herbalife expands into more countries and adds new products and new product lines, it is important to remember that the real stars of Herbalife are the products, particularly the weight-control products.

A few years ago we introduced the Thermojetics® line of products into our weight-control system. These herbal and micronutrient products combine health-building herbs from around the world to create truly unique weight-control products where you can really feel and see the difference. When we combined Thermojetics with our basic line of Cellular Nutrition products, we created a program that revolutionized the weight-control industry around the world. Today it is clear that Thermojetics does make a difference and offers people a simple and effective way to lose the extra weight they want, whether it's a few pounds, or, like a man at our 1995 The Hague Leadership weekend, over 250 pounds. Simply incredible.

Over the years I have had the good fortune to gather around me a number of experts and professionals who have helped further the Herbalife cause in many areas. One of these experts is Dr. David B. Katzin, M.D., Ph.D. the head of our Medical Advisory Board. Dr. Katzin is responsible for all the product development and testing worldwide. In 1993 I asked him to help create the *Advanced Energy Guide* to go along with the Thermojetics program. He enlisted the help of his wife, Carolyn, a nutritionist from England and a Certified Nutrition Specialist who is Vice President of Cancer Control of the Los Angeles Coastal Cities Unit of the

American Cancer Society. Together they produced the Herbalife *Advanced Energy Guide* which is a tremendous addition to understanding how to lose and maintain weight with Thermojetics.

Now Dr. Katzin and Carolyn have gone a step further and created the Herbalife *Good Eating Guide and Cookbook*. This book not only helps you understand basic nutrition, but also teaches you how to shop, cook and plan meals and has over 200 great low-fat recipes to go along with your Thermojetics program. Now it is easier than ever to cut back while really enjoying your weight-control program so you don't feel deprived or like you're making difficult sacrifices.

It has always amazed me the things people would do to themselves to lose a few extra pounds. With Thermojetics you don't have to sacrifice your health to lose weight, and with the new Herbalife *Good Eating Guide and Cookbook,* taking off those extra, unwanted pounds can be a fun and satisfying experience. I recommend the Herbalife *Good Eating Guide and Cookbook* for anyone interested in using Thermojetics to make their weight-loss dreams come true.

Introduction

by David B. Katzin, M.D., Ph.D.

Cellular Nutrition lies at the heart of Herbalife's product philosophy and has accounted for the tremendous success and acceptance of its products around the world. Modern science teaches us that health and disease are cellular processes. For each of us to have long, healthy lives, the cells of our bodies must be healthy. This means that on a daily basis the cells must receive all the nourishment they need to perform their vital functions of metabolism, growth, repair, detoxification and reproduction.

Providing the cells with the nutrition they need is more than just eating a balanced diet, although that is a start. The body must be able to digest, absorb and assimilate the nutrients in our diet before they can have a full impact on our cells. Unfortunately, most of us don't eat in a healthy manner. The food we eat is often over processed, overrefined and overcooked, all of which destroys health-building nutrition. More damaging are our poor food choices. Increasingly, we eat fast or convenience foods which are high in fat, calories, cholesterol and salt. Poor eating habits in combination with stress, illness, medication or dietary and environmental toxicity, which reduce the body's ability to digest and assimilate nutrition, mean that our body cells are faced with serious nutritional imbalances: excesses of fat, especially saturated fat, salt and cholesterol and deficiencies of key micronutrients– vitamins, minerals and trace elements–needed for good health.

The long-term result of these nutritional imbalances at a cellular level is the appearance of diet-related disease. These diseases, which include most coronary artery disease and cerebrovascular disease as well as many types of cancer, account for as much as 70% of the morbidity and mortality in our civilization. The health cost of these illnesses is staggering and the cost in terms of human loss and suffering is overwhelming. It is here that Cellular

Nutrition plays a role.

Cellular Nutrition uses three advanced nutrition technologies to improve our nutrition: food science, micronutrient supplementation and herbal science. Each of these areas contributes important nutritional factors in a form that is highly bioavailable so our body cells can reach their highest level of functioning even when there has been a history of poor eating habits, excessive dieting or illness. Formula #1 is the essence of food science. This advanced concept food is a nutritional powerhouse of protein, fiber, essential fatty acids and micronutrients. It is based on soy protein, a complete vegetarian protein rich in botanical factors called isoflavones. The exclusive protein mixture in Formula #1 provides all the amino acids our body needs in an easily digestible and assimilative form.

Micronutrient supplementation, the second aspect of Cellular Nutrition, is a precise science. One cannot simply mix vitamins and minerals together randomly or in any quantity to get a useful biological effect. Vitamins must be in balance and must be nature equivalent, similar to the forms found naturally, to have nutritional value. The same is true of herbs, the third component of Cellular Nutrition. Though herbs have been used for centuries as part of healing programs, today we know that herbs contain specific botanical factors that can enhance health and vitality. Like micronutrients, herbs must be taken in precise quantities and in balance to produce a positive nutritional effect. Improper herb choice, herb quantity or faulty handling during manufacturing of products can destroy the value of herbs or even create health hazards. All these factors are accounted for precisely in Herbalife's Cellular Nutrition products.

One area where Cellular Nutrition is extremely critical is during weight loss. Body weight is explained by the Energy Balance Equation which states that weight is stable when the energy we consume in the form of calories equals the energy output through metabolism and activity. To reduce excess weight we must consume less than our bodies burn. The most effective way to do this is through reducing caloric intake and increasing energy output. This is how Herbalife's Thermojetics weight-control program works. Using Thermojetics we create a favorable energy balance in our bodies to burn excess body fat. A cornerstone of the Thermojetics program is good nutrition, since without proper Cellular Nutrition we not only compromise our health but we can become tired and listless and decrease our energy output, thereby sabotaging our weight-control program. Thermojetics allows us to lose all the excess body fat we want in a safe and effective way without feelings of deprivation or sacrifice. The results over the years have been extraordinary.

A few years ago, at Mark's suggestion, we produced the Herbalife *Advanced Energy Guide*. This is a fat and calorie manual for individuals who wish to lose or maintain weight. It provides simple-to-use information on over 1,200 foods so our customers can learn better eating habits as part of their weight-control program. Since its introduction in 1993 it has been translated into nine languages and has helped individuals around the world with their Thermojetics programs.

The Herbalife *Good Eating Guide and Cookbook*, which is the result of hard work by my wife, Carolyn Katzin, M.S., C.N.S., an expert in the preparation of food to maintain its culinary as well as nutritional properties, takes our food knowledge a step further. Remember that food science is a key component of Cellular Nutrition and also Thermojetics. An important aspect of food is the meals we prepare and consume on our own, in addition to the shakes. To get the most out of Thermojetics, all we have to do is use the products, take shakes daily and cut back on the food we normally eat. For some this is easy, but for others it is hard and confusing. What do we cut back? How do we cut back and feel full? How do we cut back and still have our meals taste good? The Herbalife *Good Eating Guide and Cookbook* answers these questions and more.

The book begins with a discussion of basic nutrition and includes chapters on meal planning, food shopping and storage as well as meal cooking, preparation and serving. It contains over 200 recipes that will delight the palate and provide healthy, low fat meals to enhance your Thermojetics program. A meal begins long before we actually sit down to enjoy it. Planning a menu is the first step, and in the chapter on meal planning we learn the steps involved in planning a meal all the way from making a shopping list to designing the various courses including main and side dishes. The next step is shopping. In this chapter we learn about how to use our time, effort and money to our best advantage when we go to the market. We also learn about choosing and storing food to maintain freshness, nutritive value and taste.

The actual preparation of a meal can be anything from mixing a few ingredients in a shake to an elaborate dinner for two or more. We learn that each type of food has special requirements for cooking and preparation to maximize flavor and nutrition. Also included is a section on culinary herbs that add more than a savory touch to a meal, they add important botanical factors that stimulate digestive function and provide nutritive value. Most important, though, the food we eat must look, smell and taste good. All these are important aspects in getting the full enjoyment

from our meals as well as the full nutritional potential. You will find that the *Good Eating Guide and Cookbook* is much more than a cookbook, it is virtually an encyclopedia of valuable information about food, its nutritional value, its preparation and its full enjoyment.

The Herbalife *Good Eating Guide and Cookbook* is intended to be used with the Thermojetics *Advanced Energy Guide* to provide valuable insights which can make your experience of Thermojetics fun, simple and magic. It can also be used as part of a Cellular Nutrition health enhancement program to introduce delicious, low-fat meals into your regimen, since, more than ever before, we are coming to recognize the fact that we "are what we eat." The more healthful our diet, the healthier are our body cells and our bodies. Whether you are using the *Good Eating Guide and Cookbook* for weight control or good health we are sure you will find the material useful, the recipes easy to follow and the results exceptional.

Whatever your nutritional goals are in Herbalife, Carolyn and I on behalf of Mark Hughes and Herbalife wish you success and a long, happy and healthy life!

Chapter One

The Herbalife Good Nutrition Guide

- Nutrients and their functions, sources and recommended intakes

- Protein and amino acids; fat and fatty acids; carbohydrate and dietary fiber

- Vitamins; minerals and trace elements; antioxidants and functional nutrients

INTRODUCTION

The Herbalife *Good Eating Guide and Cookbook* is designed to complement the entire range of Herbalife nutrition programs from weight control to fitness to increasing bulk and muscle. This guide will provide you with all of the information necessary for making healthy food choices. When used in conjunction with the basic product line and the *Advanced Energy Guide* you will find that achieving and maintaining a healthy weight is easy and fun.

Cellular Nutrition is the ingestion, digestion and absorption as well as the assimilation of food in order to nourish each individual cell of the body. In this book we will focus on the composition and nutritional value of food. You will learn which foods have the richest amount of nutrients and which ones the poorest. You will also learn what nutrients can do for your body's cells and why we need to consume them on a regular basis for optimal health.

Nutrients are described as essential if we need to consume them every day in order to avoid deficiencies. Let us review those essential nutrients we need and which foods are rich in them.

■ PROTEIN AND AMINO ACIDS; FAT AND FATTY ACIDS; CARBOHYDRATE AND DIETARY FIBER

■ PROTEIN AND AMINO ACIDS

Protein provides nitrogen to our body in the form of individual amino acids. There are twenty-one amino acids commonly found in foods and nine of these must be consumed on a regular basis as the body cannot make them itself. The "essential" or "indispensable" amino acids are the branched chain amino acids, valine, isoleucine and leucine; the aromatic amino acids, phenylalanine and tryptophan; and the sulfur containing amino acid, methionine. The other essential amino acids are lysine, histidine and threonine.

Protein is used to maintain and repair all the cells of our body. It is an important component of the immune system and an insufficient intake of essential amino acids results in an increased vulnerability to disease. Protein also forms muscle, bone and other structural elements and provides the building materials for the intermediates needed for proper functioning of our cells such as hormones and enzymes.

In addition, protein provides energy, and when consumed in amounts over and above what can be used for tissue repair, it provides approximately the same number of calories as carbohydrate, four calories per gram. The amount of protein in meat, fish, poultry and milk solids is between 15 and 40 percent. Plant sources such as cooked cereals and breads, beans and peas contain between three and 10 percent. Another important source of protein is the soy bean which is used in Herbalife's Formula #1 in a highly digestible form called soy isolate.

The amount of protein each person requires will depend upon various circumstances. For most people under normal healthy conditions this is approximately one gram per kilogram ideal body weight (about 50-75 grams) or between two and three servings of a protein rich food each day. A three ounce serving of meat, fish or poultry is about the size of a deck of cards. Other serving sizes include a half cup of cooked beans, one whole egg or two tablespoons of peanut butter. During pregnancy a woman requires more protein and she should increase her intake by 10 grams per day. During lactation a mother needs to consume a little more protein especially during the first six months in order to prevent depletion of her own body stores of essential amino acids. Another situation that requires additional protein is when the body is extremely stressed such

as during an infection, if burned, suffering a traumatic injury or undergoing surgery.

■ FAT AND FATTY ACIDS

Although we all know that eating too much fat puts on unwanted weight and that many foods taste good because of the fat in them, we may not be as aware that fat in small quantities is essential for life. Just as with protein, there are certain components of fat that are essential as we cannot synthesize or make them in our bodies. These essential fatty acids are found in many oils (an oil is a fat that is liquid at room temperature) made from nuts, seeds and certain fruits like olives and avocados. Fat is a concentrated source of energy providing nine calories per gram, more than twice as many calories as either protein or carbohydrate. It provides an energy store and also serves to insulate and protect vital organs such as the kidneys and heart. In addition, fat provides a vehicle for the storage and absorption of the fat soluble vitamins A, D, E and K (see pages 25 and 26 for a fuller description of these).

The chemical structure of fat is three fatty acids attached to a glycerol backbone. The fatty acids vary in carbon chain length and degree of saturation and this gives a fat or oil its character. When the carbon chain is long and there are many bonds that are unsaturated, the fatty acid is called poly- (meaning "many") unsaturated. If there is only one place where additional hydrogen can be added to make the chain saturated, the fatty acid is described as mono- (meaning "one") unsaturated. If the chain is completely saturated and has no double bonds, it is called a saturated fatty acid.

Examples of polyunsaturated fatty acid rich oils include sunflower seed oil and safflower seed oil. Polyunsaturated oils run thinly at room temperature and will not harden in the refrigerator.

Examples of monounsaturated fatty acid rich oils include olive oil, peanut oil and canola (or rapeseed) oil. These may become cloudy in the refrigerator but are liquid at room temperature.

A fat that contains many saturated fatty acids is hard at room temperature and in the refrigerator. Examples of such fats are lard and butter. As mentioned above, a fat that is liquid at room temperature is described as an oil.

A diet that contains too much saturated fats is associated with many of the diseases that afflict modern society. Most saturated fat is derived from animals and form the basis of the typical American diet. We need to consume less of these fats found in meats and dairy produce, and more of those from vegetables, nuts, seeds and fruits in order to prevent the onset of such degenerative disorders as cardiovascular disease, stroke and certain cancers like prostate, breast and colon. Many of the saturated animal fats are associated with cholesterol and the over consumption of both results in an elevation of a protein called LDL (low-density lipoprotein) that transports them in the blood as well as free cholesterol. HDL (high-density lipoprotein) is sometimes called the "good" cholesterol because studies indicate that a relatively higher quantity of this lipoprotein compared with LDL provides a better degree of protection from cardiovascular disease. Vegetarians and those who consume small quantities of animal protein usually have a favorable ratio of LDL-cholesterol to HDL-cholesterol and have a similarly reduced risk of heart disease and stroke.

Fatty acid composition is also related to our immune system and protection from disease. We can classify a fatty acid by where the double bonds occur. If a double bond is at the end of the carbon chain it is described as an omega-3 (omega means "end" in Greek) or n-3. fatty acid. If the first double bond counting from the n-terminal is at the next location down it is called an omega-6 or n-6. We cannot make enough linoleic acid (an omega-6 fatty acid) and we cannot insert the n-3 position of a double bond so we need to consume these fatty acids regularly. We need at least four percent of our daily diet from these essential fatty acids. The ratio of omega-6 to omega-3 fatty acids is about three or four times higher in a typical American diet compared with a

vegetarian one. When a diet is too high in total fat as well as an increase in the proportion coming from animal-derived omega-6 fatty acids compared with vegetable-source omega-3 fatty acids, there is an increased risk of stroke and certain inflammatory processes in the body. For optimal health of your immune system you should increase the amount of healthy vegetable oils in your diet at the expense of the animal fats so that the ratio of omega-6 to omega-3 is closer to five to one than its current 15 or 20 to one.

Trans fatty acids are the result of commercial hardening of oils to form margarine, mayonnaise and other food products. The oils are described as "partially hydrogenated" as hydrogen is added to the oil to harden them. These trans fatty acids should not comprise more than a very small fraction of your diet as they are handled at best like saturated fat and may be damaging to your health.

Many flavors are dissolved in fats and make a food taste good. The essential oils of plants are so aromatic that they form the base of perfume and provide small quantities of herbs and spices with their rich aroma. We can lower the fat in our diet when we use more herbs and spices to provide flavor. On page 57 of Chapter Two we provide you with suggestions for substituting fat in various recipes.

■ CARBOHYDRATE AND DIETARY FIBER

Our bodies burn carbohydrate as the major source of fuel. This provides four calories per gram of energy and is found as starches and sugars in food, nearly all of which come from plants. Grains, fruits and vegetables provide carbohydrate in our diet that is further digested to form glucose and fructose in the blood.

Starch or Complex Carbohydrate

Sugars link together in plants to form a stored energy source called starch. Complex carbohydrates include starch as well as dietary fiber (see next page) as they need to be broken down into their constituent sugars by digestive enzymes. This slows down the absorption of glucose into the blood stream after a meal and provides a more even flow of energy to the body.

Glucose

The brain relies on glucose for its function and we feel light headed and dizzy if it should fall too low in our bloodstream. Usually glucose is kept within a certain range with the help of the pancreatic hormone insulin. A defect in the action of insulin results in diabetes which can be a life-threatening disease. All of our cells require energy and glucose is the form most commonly used. If we eat more carbohydrate than we require for fuel we can store a small quantity of it in our liver and muscle as glycogen, but once this capacity is reached, the excess is converted to fat. *It is the combination of a diet that contains too much fat and too much sugar that results in most of the overweight and obesity we see.*

Fructose

This is also called fruit sugar because it occurs mainly in fruits. Fructose is very sweet and does not require insulin to be used by the cells. Herbalife's Formula #1 uses fructose as a sweetener.

Simple Sugars and Refined Carbohydrate

Sucrose or table sugar is composed of glucose and fructose together. It is metabolized very rapidly and provides energy for the cells. Refined carbohydrate is starch that has been partially digested so that it forms simple sugars quickly and is absorbed rapidly. Sugars taste good and often encourage us to eat more than we need for energy. Too much sugar also causes tooth decay.

Dietary Fiber

Certain sugars and starches are not digestible to humans because they do not have the necessary enzymes. These are called dietary fiber and they form bulk in our diet that maintains the health of the colon. Most people do not consume sufficient dietary fiber because they do not eat enough whole grains, fruits and vegetables. A healthy intake of dietary fiber is between 25 and 35 grams per day, spread out over the three main meals to give the colon an optimal amount at all times. Eating in excess of 40 grams per day may reduce the absorption of minerals from food and is not recommended.

Dietary Fiber

Excellent sources of Dietary Fiber (4-5 grams per serving)	Good sources of Dietary Fiber (2-4 grams per serving)
BREADS AND CEREALS	**BREADS AND CEREALS**
Bread and other cereals containing 4-5 grams Dietary Fiber per serving (read the product label)	Bread and other cereals containing 2-4 grams Dietary Fiber per serving (read the product label)
VEGETABLES	**VEGETABLES**
Beans, baked, canned (½ Cup)	Carrots (1) Potato, baked (1)
Beans, soaked and boiled (½ Cup)	Spinach (½ Cup) Sweet potato (1)
Lima beans, boiled, drained (½ Cup)	Brussels sprouts (8) Beans, yellow or green (½ Cup)
FRUIT	**FRUIT**
Apricots, dried halves (6)	Apple (1)
Prune, dried, raw (6) Figs, dried (2)	Berries, blue or raspberries (½ Cup) Orange (1)
NUTS	
Almonds (½ Cup)	**NUTS**
Brazil nuts (½ Cup) Peanuts (½ Cup)	Walnuts (½ Cup)

■ VITAMINS

Vitamins are essential for all higher animals to exist. We require 13 major vitamins to regulate functions within each cell of the body. These are categorized according to their solubility in fat or in water and relates to the length of time that they can be stored in the body. The fat soluble vitamins A, D, E and K can be stored in the liver and fat tissues and it takes several months for a deficiency symptom to occur if these vitamins are depleted. The water soluble vitamins, the eight B vitamins are identified as thiamin (vitamin B1); riboflavin (vitamin B2); niacin (vitamin B3); pantothenic acid (vitamin B5); pyridoxine (vitamin B6); vitamin B12; biotin; and folacin. Vitamin C or ascorbic acid is also water soluble. These vitamins are stored for only a short period of time and need to be consumed more frequently than the fat soluble ones for optimal health. Most vitamins are sensitive to destruction by light and heat so that their storage, handling and cooking need to prevent this loss as much as possible.

Vitamin A (Retinol)

FUNCTIONS: growth and repair of body tissues, reproductive health, vision and health of the retina.
SOURCES: fish liver oils, liver, kidney, milk, cream, cheese.
RDA: Men: 1,000 micrograms Retinol Equivalents (5,000 IU) Women: 800 micrograms RE (4,000 IU)
TOXICITY: Over 5,000 IU per day in some people may be toxic if taken as supplements of vitamin A as retinol.

Beta Carotene and other Carotenoids

FUNCTIONS: antioxidants, pro-vitamin A.
SOURCES: dark green leafy vegetables, carrots, cantaloupe melon.
TOXICITY: none. The body regulates the amount of vitamin A formed.

Vitamin D (Cholecalciferol)

FUNCTIONS: maintenance of calcium and phosphorus levels in blood. Bone health.
SOURCES: fortified milk, butter, margarine, cheese, cream, fish, oysters and fortified cereals. Also from the action of sunlight on skin.

RDA: Adults: 5 micrograms (200 IU)
TOXICITY: like vitamin A this vitamin can be toxic if taken to excess in supplements or by consuming fish liver in large quantities. Toxic symptoms may occur above 45 micrograms (1,800 IU) per day, particularly if associated with excessive amounts of vitamin A.

Vitamin E (Tocopherol)
FUNCTIONS: antioxidant, has a role in protecting cell membranes and may prevent heart disease.
SOURCES: vegetable oils, especially when cold pressed; wheat germ, corn, nuts, seeds, olives, asparagus, spinach and other green leafy vegetables.
RDA: increases with the quantity of polyunsaturated fats in the diet (PUFAs)
MEN: 10 milligrams or 10 alpha-tocopherol equivalents (TE)
WOMEN: 8 milligrams (8 alpha-tocopherol equivalents)
TOXICITY: possibly none, although some researchers feel that daily consumption of more than 8,000 milligrams may result in tiredness and headaches.

Vitamin K
FUNCTIONS: an essential component of blood clotting.
SOURCES: cabbage, cauliflower, spinach, cereals, vegetable oils. About 80% of our needs is provided by bacteria in the intestines.
RDA: Men: 80 micrograms
Women: 65 micrograms
TOXICITY: none.

Thiamin (Vitamin B-1)
FUNCTIONS: metabolism, nervous function.
SOURCES: unrefined cereal grains, wheat germ, liver, lean cuts of pork, beans, seeds and nuts.
RDA: Men: 1.5 milligrams
Women: 1.0 milligrams
TOXICITY: none.

Riboflavin (Vitamin B-2)
FUNCTIONS: metabolism, red cell formation, skin and visual health
SOURCES: milk and other dairy products, lean meats, eggs, nuts, green leafy vegetables, beans and fortified grain products.
RDA: Men: 1.7 milligrams
Women: 1.3 milligrams
TOXICITY: none.

Niacin (Vitamin B-3)
FUNCTIONS: normal functioning of skin, nerves and

digestive system, blood circulation.
SOURCES: meats, milk and
eggs (from conversion of
tryptophan to niacin)
RDA: Men: 19 milligrams
Niacin Equivalents (NE)
WOMEN: 15 milligrams Niacin
Equivalents (NE)
TOXICITY: none in the form of
nicotinamide. Niacin may cause
flushing, rashes and liver
damage. Medical supervision is
needed if niacin is taken for its
cholesterol lowering properties
in pharmacological doses.

Pantothenic Acid (Vitamin B-5)

FUNCTIONS: metabolism,
development of the central
nervous system.
SOURCES: widespread in foods;
"pantothenic" means widespread
RDA: none. Safe and adequate
dietary intake estimated at 4-7
milligrams per day.
TOXICITY: none.

Pyridoxine (Vitamin B-6)

FUNCTIONS: metabolism,
immune function.
SOURCES: chicken, fish,
kidney, liver, pork, eggs, whole
unrefined grains, peanuts,
walnuts and soybeans.
RDA: Men: 2 milligrams

Women: 1.6 milligrams
TOXICITY: possibly over 100
milligrams per day as a
supplement over time may cause
nerve symptoms including
dizziness, tingling and headache.

Vitamin B-12

FUNCTIONS: red cell
formation, central nervous
system maintenance.
SOURCES: milk and milk
products, eggs, poultry, shellfish.
Synthesized by intestinal bacteria.
Requires intrinsic factor from
gastric secretions for absorption.
RDA: Adults: 2.0 micrograms
TOXICITY: none.

Folacin (Folate or Folic Acid)

FUNCTIONS: red cell formation,
new tissue growth (important in
early stages of pregnancy).
SOURCES: dark green, leafy
vegetables (Folacin comes from
the Latin word *folium* for leaf),
citrus fruits and juices, beans
and other legumes, whole
unrefined cereals.
RDA: Men: 200 micrograms
WOMEN: 180 micrograms
Requirements increased by
smokers. Women who may become
pregnant should consume at least
400 micrograms per day to

reduce the risk of neural tube defects (spina bifida) in their babies.
TOXICITY: none.

Biotin

FUNCTIONS: metabolism, hair health.
SOURCES: liver, egg yolk, soy. Synthesized by intestinal bacteria.
RDA: none. The safe and adequate range of dietary intake is 30 to 100 micrograms per day.
TOXICITY: none.

■ MINERALS AND TRACE ELEMENTS

The cells of our bodies need minerals for their structure and to help the processes of metabolism. All enzymes require minerals or trace elements as cofactors assisting them in their actions. There are more than 60 minerals present in the body making up about four percent of its total weight. Twenty two of these are considered essential and must be consumed on a regular basis for optimal health and to avoid deficiencies. Minerals are the basic elements of life and six of these are required in relatively large quantities by the body. These are calcium, magnesium,

sodium, potassium, phosphorus and sulfur. Other minerals that are required in smaller quantities are called trace elements. These are boron, chloride, chromium, copper, iodine, iron, manganese, molybdenum, selenium, silicon, vanadium and zinc. Minerals that occur in the body in minute quantities include arsenic, cadmium, cobalt, lead, lithium and tin. These are not recommended as supplements to foods.

Calcium

FUNCTIONS: formation and maintenance of bones and teeth. Regulation of heart and other muscle contractions. Necessary for blood clotting.
SOURCES: milk and milk products, dark green leafy vegetables, broccoli, canned fish, fortified cereal products.
RDA: Adults: 800 milligrams
TOXICITY: none. Absorption regulated by vitamin D. Constipation may occur if intake exceeds 2,500 milligrams per day.

Magnesium

FUNCTIONS: metabolism, nerve and muscle function including heart muscle, red cell maintenance.
SOURCES: whole, unrefined

cereal grains, nuts, legumes, green leafy vegetables, bananas.
RDA: Men: 350 milligrams
WOMEN: 280 milligrams
TOXICITY: none unless kidney function impaired. Large amounts more than 1000 milligrams per day are not recommended as supplements.

Sodium
FUNCTIONS: regulates blood pressure and water balance.
SOURCES: widely distributed in nature. Processed, preserved and salted foods contain high levels.
RDA: none. Most adults consume more than the approximately 500 milligrams per day needed. Safe and adequate dietary intakes should restrict the intake to no more than 4,000 milligrams per day.
TOXICITY: none unless kidney function impaired.

Potassium
FUNCTIONS: muscle contractions, nerve impulses and proper functioning of the heart and kidneys.
SOURCES: most foods, citrus fruits, bananas, potato skins, yogurt, meat, poultry.
RDA: none. Reported intakes range between 1,600 and 6,000 milligrams per day with vegetarians consuming higher amounts.

TOXICITY: none unless kidney function impaired.

Phosphorus
FUNCTIONS: formation and maintenance of bones and teeth, metabolism.
SOURCES: most foods, fish, meat, poultry, dairy products, eggs, peas, beans, nuts.
RDA: Adults: 800 milligrams
TOXICITY: none. Safe up to 4,500 milligrams per day. The ratio of calcium to phosphorus is important and should be equal to approximately 1.0.

Sulfur
FUNCTIONS: component of insulin, also of hair, skin and nails. As part of glutathione it acts as an antioxidant.
SOURCES: in protein foods as sulfur amino acids, cysteine, methionine and taurine.
RDA: satisfied by essential amino acid requirements.
TOXICITY: none in foods. Supplemental methionine may be toxic.

■ TRACE ELEMENTS
Boron
FUNCTIONS: bone formation in conjunction with calcium, magnesium and phosphorus

steroid hormone production.
SOURCES: apples, pears, broccoli, carrots and other fruits and vegetables.
RDA: none. Usual range of intake is 0.4 to 1.9 milligrams per day.
TOXICITY: above 50 milligrams per day may interfere with riboflavin and phosphorus metabolism and supplements are not recommended above 2 milligrams per day.

Chlorine (chloride)
FUNCTIONS: fluid and acid-base balance, gastric juice component.
SOURCES: with sodium in table salt, preserved foods and fish.
RDA: none. Usual intake is in range of 4.5 to 6.5 milligrams per day.
TOXICITY: none in healthy persons.

Chromium
FUNCTIONS: metabolism of carbohydrate and fat. A component of glucose tolerance factor associated with the action of insulin.
SOURCES: brewer's yeast, whole unrefined grains, wheat germ, meat, fortified cereals.
RDA: range of 50 to 200 micrograms for adults as a safe and adequate intake.
TOXICITY: none, or very low from sources found in foods (as the trivalent form).

Copper
FUNCTIONS: formation of red blood cells, maintenance of bones, blood vessels, nerves and immune system.
SOURCES: shellfish (especially oysters), beans, nuts, organ meats, whole grains.
RDA: none. Usual range of intake 1.2 to 1.6 milligrams per day.
TOXICITY: safe up to 0.5 milligrams per kilogram body weight per day.

Iodine (iodide)
FUNCTIONS: metabolism, thyroid function.
SOURCES: seafood, seaweed, dairy products, crops grown in iodine-rich soils, iodized salt.
RDA: 150 micrograms
TOXICITY: safe up to 2 milligrams per day.

Iron
FUNCTIONS: component of hemoglobin in red cells and myoglobin in muscle. Cofactor of many enzymes.
SOURCES: liver, kidney, red meat, egg yolk, dried fruit, enriched pasta and breads, fortified cereals. Better absorbed if vitamin C also present.
RDA: Men: 10 milligrams

Women: 15 milligrams
TOXICITY: safe in healthy persons up to 25 milligrams per day. Iron overload may occur in genetically at risk individuals or if high levels consumed over long periods such as if cooking in iron pots on a daily basis.

Manganese
FUNCTIONS: metabolism, bone formation, reproduction.
SOURCES: whole grains and cereal products, fruits, vegetables, tea.
RDA: none. Safe and adequate range of intake 2 to 5 milligrams.
TOXICITY: safe up to 8 milligrams per day. Excess manganese may interfere with iron absorption.

Molybdenum
FUNCTIONS: metabolism, nervous system, good health.
SOURCES: liver, whole grains, beans, leafy vegetables.
RDA: none. Safe and adequate range of intake 75 to 250 micrograms.
TOXICITY: Excess molybdenum interferes with copper metabolism. Safe up to 10 milligrams per day.

Selenium
FUNCTIONS: antioxidant as component of glutathione peroxidase, also with vitamin E; immune function, heart and muscle function.
SOURCES: seafood, kidney, liver, Brazil nuts.
RDA: Men: 70 micrograms
Women: 55 micrograms
TOXICITY: safe up to 750 micrograms per day.

Silicon
FUNCTIONS: formation of bone matrix, collagen, and cartilage.
SOURCES: cereal grains, chicken skin, beer.
RDA: none known. Essentiality acknowledged.
TOXICITY: none known.

Zinc
FUNCTIONS: cofactor for many enzymes, metabolism, reproduction, cell growth and healing, immune function.
SOURCES: shellfish (especially oysters), liver, meat, egg yolk, whole grains, wheat germ, soy.
RDA: Men: 15 milligrams
Women: 12 milligrams

■ WATER
Of all of the nutrients listed here, water is the most essential to life. Without oxygen we die within a

few minutes; without water we cannot live more than a few days. Minerals and other nutrients dissolve in it and bodily functions occur in solution with it. Water is distributed throughout the body and is maintained at a fairly constant level by hormones that adapt the kidney function, thirst mechanisms and intestinal uptake and release.

Water is consumed in several ways; first, as the liquid itself, secondly, as a solvent in other fluids, and thirdly, as a component of food. In the process of digesting, absorbing and releasing energy from food, water is released as a product of metabolism. Water is lost from the body by forming digestive juices, as part of urine and feces, and as part of expired air. Perspiration is another and variable way that water is lost from the body. An athlete exercising in a hot and dry environment may lose as much as four pounds of water weight during a practice.

We have no provision for storing water in the body so it must be taken in regularly to make up for the necessary losses described above. Babies and small children lose water faster than adults as their body composition has a higher water content outside of the cells.

Diarrhea or vomiting in a small infant requires immediate medical attention as this can be fatal if not checked. Oral rehydration therapy is a way of adding water, sugar and salt back to an infant to help prevent further water loss. In adults, too, diarrhea and vomiting may result in dehydration and should not be ignored. Signs of dehydration include feeling dizzy or lightheaded, nausea, fatigue, thirst and/or headache. Don't always rely on thirst to prevent dehydration. Prevention is always the best way; drink water frequently throughout the day and especially when exercising.

Your intake of water should vary with the climate, quantity of fruits and vegetables consumed, and your physical activity. As a general rule, we recommend between six and eight glasses (eight fluid ounce size) of water or non-caffeinated fluids per day. The food you consume will provide you with the rest of your daily needs for water as long as you consume at least five servings (one medium item; one cup of raw; half cup of cooked) of fruits and vegetables each day. Here is a list of the water content of various foods.

Percentage Water of Some Foods

Lettuce	96
Celery	95
Watermelon	92
Broccoli	91
Milk	88
Carrots	87
Hot cereals	85
Apples	84
Fish	78
Eggs	75
Bananas	74
Roast chicken	67
Roast beef	59
Bread, white	37
Butter	16
Nuts	4
Soda crackers	4
Sugar	1
Oils	0

There is an upper limit to how much water is healthy. We do not recommend consuming more than 12 cups in a 24 hour period on a regular basis. Anything in excess, including water, can be harmful.

■ ANTIOXIDANTS & FUNCTIONAL NUTRIENTS

We are learning new facts about this exciting category of nutrients each day. All of the Herbalife products include several of these "functional" nutrients from natural sources.

Antioxidants are natural defenders; they protect against cellular damage from free radicals. Free radicals are formed during normal metabolism and are increased during an infection, as a result of stress or trauma, during intense exercise or after drinking alcohol. Free radicals are also formed as a result of exposure to environmental hazards like tobacco smoke, radiation from X-rays and sunlight, exhaust fumes and exposure to toxic herbicides, pesticides or carcinogens.

Free radicals can attack all body tissues, degrade collagen and reprogram DNA. Oxygenated free radicals are unstable molecules with an extra electron that seeks a pair from surrounding molecules. Antioxidants provide an extra electron and prevent damage at the same time. Anticarcinogens are similarly protective of DNA found in the nucleus of each cell.

Antioxidants and anticarcinogens have chemical structures that allow the extra electron to be "dampened" or "quenched". There are many naturally-occurring substances with structures that provide this action and we are only just beginning to identify which ones are the most effective. Because plants cannot move around to avoid dangers, these have high concentrations of protective elements. We can look to the plant kingdom, and in particular, to herbs for protection against environmental hazards. There are over 4,000 compounds called flavonoids in fruits, vegetables, grains and herbs. They are called bioflavonoids, isoflavones and flavones, depending upon the way they are classified. These usually occur with vitamin C, for instance, in the white pithy part of citrus fruit. Pycnogenols are flavonoid compounds that have about five to fifteen times the antioxidant activity of vitamin C.

Botanical factors include the colored compounds called carotenes. Beta carotene is best known because of its ability to split into two molecules of Vitamin A (as retinol). Other carotenes form the yellow and green colors of vegetables and fruits and have antioxidant activity, an example is lycopene found in tomatoes. There are about 500 carotenes identified in the plant kingdom.

Fruits, vegetables, culinary herbs and spices are all excellent sources of botanical factors with antioxidant and other beneficial nutrient functions. A healthy diet includes a wide variety of these functional nutrients. We recommend consuming at least five servings of fruits and vegetables each day, and a generous quantity of culinary herbs like parsley, rosemary, thyme, marjoram, etc. as well as spices like cumin, turmeric and coriander added to the food you cook.

■ HERBALIFE'S GOOD NUTRITION ADVICE

- Eat a wide variety of foods.
- Include dark green and yellow vegetables often (at least once a day).

- Include cruciferous vegetables (broccoli, cabbage, cauliflower, etc.) several times each week.
- Include extra virgin olive oil as a source of fat.
- Consume high fat foods (See Advanced Energy Guide) not more than twice a week.
- Consume medium fat foods (25-40% calories from fat) not more than twice each day.
- Consume low fat foods the rest of the time.
- Be moderate in consumption of alcohol (not more than one glass of wine or beer each day).
- Emphasize whole grain foods such as brown rice, whole wheat bread, pasta in place of processed foods like white rice or white bread.
- Choose several fiber-containing foods each day (see table on page 24).
- Emphasize foods from plants rather than those foods from animal sources.
- Use Herbalife nutritional shakes and supplement tablets as recommended.

THE FOOD PYRAMID

The Dietary Guidelines, Fourth Edition published in 1995, emphasize the importance of a diet with plenty of grain products, vegetables and fruits. The Food Guide Pyramid shows how to select from the five major food groups with smaller amounts coming from animal products, fats and oils.

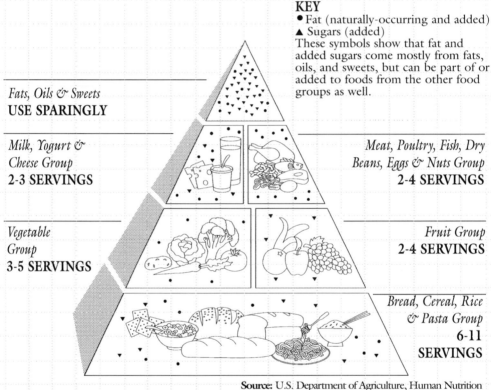

KEY
● Fat (naturally-occurring and added)
▲ Sugars (added)
These symbols show that fat and added sugars come mostly from fats, oils, and sweets, but can be part of or added to foods from the other food groups as well.

Fats, Oils & Sweets
USE SPARINGLY

Milk, Yogurt &
Cheese Group
2-3 SERVINGS

Meat, Poultry, Fish, Dry
Beans, Eggs & Nuts Group
2-4 SERVINGS

Vegetable
Group
3-5 SERVINGS

Fruit Group
2-4 SERVINGS

Bread, Cereal, Rice
& Pasta Group
6-11
SERVINGS

Source: U.S. Department of Agriculture, Human Nutrition Information Service, August 1992, Leaflet No. 572

A modified Food Pyramid has been suggested by the Harvard School of Public Health and the World Health Organization. This recognizes the value of olive oil in the diet by placing it just above the fruits and vegetable section. Wine with a meal is also an optional recommendation (one glass for women and two for men). The new guidelines recognize the enjoyment of food and has a more positive approach than previous versions. Another difference in the new guidelines is the incorporation of physical activity in maintaining a steady and healthy body weight.

SERVING SIZE

WHAT COUNTS AS A SERVING

Grain Products Group (bread, cereal, rice and pasta)

- 1 slice of bread
- 1 ounce of ready-to-eat cereal
- ½ cup of cooked cereal, rice or pasta

Vegetable Group

- 1 cup of raw leafy vegetables
- ½ cup of other vegetables (cooked or chopped raw)
- ¾ cup of vegetable juice

Fruit Group

- * 1 medium apple, banana, orange
- ½ cup of chopped, cooked, or canned fruit

Milk Group (milk, yogurt and cheese)

- 1 cup of milk or yogurt
- 1½ ounces of natural cheese
- 2 ounces of processed cheese

Meat and Beans Group (meat, poultry, fish, dry beans, eggs and nuts)

- 2-3 ounces of cooked lean meat, poultry or fish
- ½ cup of cooked dry beans or 1 egg counts as 1 ounce of lean meat.
  2 tablespoons of peanut butter or ⅓ cup of nuts count as 1 ounce of meat.

Now that you have the basic information about nutrition, you can put it into practice by using this cookbook. There are many ways to use Cellular Nutrition: For weight loss you might take two shakes a day and have one main meal of 400-600 calories, using recipes from the fish, meat, poultry or vegetarian sections. For weight control, we recommend one shake a day and two main meals plus fruit snacks.

Sample seven-day menu plans for 1200, 1500 and 2000 calories per day using recipes from this book follow. Remember, always take your Herbalife supplement tablets as recommended.

Herbalife *Good Eating Guide and Cookbook* recipes provide an average of 25% calories from fat. They provide you with a wide range of food choices rich in nutrients, high in dietary fiber and delicious to eat. Create your menus with the food pyramid in mind so the majority of your energy is coming from plant-based foods such as grains, beans, vegetables and fruits.

Seven Day Meal Plans

1200 CALORIES

Day 1

Breakfast	Aloha Delight Shake	Page..179
Lunch	Turkeyburgers	
	Southwestern Style	Page..289
	Celery and carrot sticks	
Snack	1 orange	
Dinner	Pasta and Eggplant	Page..270
	Provençale Salad	Page..299
	Pears in Red Wine	Page..224

Day 2

Breakfast	Wild-Berry Orange Shake	Page..195
Lunch	Green Pea Soup	Page..325
	Citrus Salad	Page..294
	Sourdough roll	
Snack	1 banana	
Dinner	Ginger-Sesame Salmon	Page..232
	Brown Rice Pilaf	Page..263
	Steamed broccoli	
	Peach Frozen Yogurt	Page..223

Day 3

Breakfast	¾ Cup Bran Flakes	
	1 Cup skim milk	
	½ Cup fresh blueberries	
Lunch	Gazpacho	Page..324
	Chef's Salad	Page..293
	2 ginger cookies	Page..205
Snack	1 fresh apple	
Dinner	Vegetarian Stew	Page..349
	Green salad with	
	cucumber and	
	yogurt dressing	Page..310
	Peach Crumble	Page..222

Day 4

Breakfast	Mocha Shake	Page..187
Lunch	Tomato Soup	Page..332
	1 whole wheat dinner roll	
	Tabbouleh	Page..302
Snack	2 dried apricot halves	
Dinner	Beef Bourguignon	Page..249
	Brussels sprouts and	
	Chestnuts	Page..335
	Brown rice	
	Lemon Sherbet	Page..220

Day 5

Breakfast   Fruit-Juicy Shake   Page..182

Lunch   Chicken Soup   Page..322
Carrot and Raisin Salad   Page..292
1 whole wheat dinner roll

Snack   1 banana

Dinner   Mexican Bean Pie   Page..174
Green Salad with
Spicy Yogurt Dressing   Page..317
Apple Crisp   Page..215

Day 6

Breakfast   Herbal All-Bran Shake   Page..184

Lunch   Grilled Tuna   Page..233
Warm Coriander Sauce   Page..319
Garlic Mashed Potatoes   Page..340
French Peas   Page..338
Fresh Fruit Salad   Page..217

Snack   1 orange

Dinner   Stir-Fry Vegetables and
Rice   Page..276
Pineapple Meringue Pie   Page..209

Day 7

Breakfast   ½ fresh grapefruit
1 slice whole grain wheat toast
1 teaspoon butter
Frittata with Spinach   Page..339

Lunch   3 Bean Mexican Salad   Page..291
Fresh Peaches in
Lemon Juice   Page..218

Snack   1 plum

Dinner   Chicken with Tarragon   Page..282
Glazed Carrots   Page..341
Mixed Berry Sherbet   Page..221

1500 CALORIES

Day 1

Breakfast	Apple Pie Shake	Page..179
Lunch	Macaroni and Cheese	Page..266
	Green Salad with	
	Vinaigrette Dressing	Page..318
	1 whole wheat dinner roll	
	1 fresh pear	
Snack	2 dried apricot halves	
Dinner	Whitefish with Ginger	
	and Lemon	Page..246
	Glazed Carrots	Page..341
	Mixed Berry Sherbet	Page..221
	1 Chocolate Chip	
	Cookie	Page..203

Day 2

Breakfast	Banana Fruit Shake	Page..180
Lunch	Gazpacho	Page..324
	Lentil Patty with	Page..172
	cucumber and	
	yogurt dressing	Page..310
	1 sourdough roll	
Snack	1 orange	
Dinner	Mushrooms	
	a la Grecque	Page..160
	Turkey Breast in	
	White Wine Sauce	Page..287
	Garlic Mashed Potatoes	Page..340
	Apple Crisp	Page..215
	Nonfat whipped cream	

Day 3

Breakfast	Strawberry	
	Sensation Shake	Page..194
Lunch	Spicy Bean Chili	Page..177
	Celery and carrot sticks	
	1 banana	
Snack	1 slice Zucchini Bread	Page..212
Dinner	Oven-Baked	
	Sesame Chicken	Page..286
	Green Salad with	
	Lemon Tahini	
	Dressing	Page..312
	Peach Crumble	Page..222

Day 4

Breakfast	1 cup shredded wheat	
	1 cup skim milk	
	½ cup strawberries or blueberries	
Lunch	Chicken & Okra Gumbo	Page..321
	Greek Salad	Page..297
	1 slice Soda Bread	Page..210
	Lemon Sherbet	Page..220
Snack	1 banana	
Dinner	Bruschetta	Page..152
	Spaghetti with	
	Artichoke Hearts	Page..275
	Green Salad with	
	Vinaigrette Dressing	Page..318
	1 Ginger Cookie	Page..205

Day 5

Breakfast	Prune Shake	Page..191
Lunch	Grilled Chicken Breast Sandwich	Page..305
	Carrot and celery sticks	
Snack	1 apple	
Dinner	Spinach, Brown Rice and Tofu	Page..345
	Green Salad with Oriental Dressing	Page..314
	Key Lime Pie	Page..206

Day 6

Breakfast	Coffee Shake	Page..181
Lunch	Salmon and Scallops Brochettes	Page..236
	Green Salad with Oriental Dressing	Page..314
Snack	1 orange	
Dinner	Navy Bean Stew	Page..175
	1 slice Soda Bread	Page..210
	2 Apricot Almond Squares	Page..198

Day 7

Breakfast	Orange Blossom Shake	Page..188
Lunch	Tuna Sandwich on Rye	Page..308
	Carrot and celery sticks	
	2 Ginger Cookies	Page..205
Snack	1 apple	
Dinner	Minestrone	Page..328
	Chicken Cacciatore	Page..279
	Green Salad with Vinaigrette Dressing	Page..318
	1 whole wheat dinner roll	
	Peach Frozen Yogurt	Page..223

2000 CALORIES

Day 1

Breakfast Cappuccino Shake Page..181

Lunch Yogurt Soup with Mint Page..333
Chicken Salad Sandwich Page..305
Carrot and celery sticks

Snack 2 dried apricot halves

Dinner Sun-dried Tomato
Meatloaf Page..257
Green Salad with Low-
Oriental Dressing Page..314
Mixed Berry Sherbet Page..221
2 Chocolate Chip Cookies Page..203

Day 2

Breakfast Pear Shake Page..190

Lunch Tomato Soup Page..332
1 whole wheat dinner roll
Shepherd's Pie Page..255
Glazed Carrots Page..341

Snack 1 orange

Dinner Ceviche Page..153
Pasta and Eggplant Page..270
Mixed Salad with
Vinaigrette Dressing Page..318
Lemon Sherbet Page..220

Day 3

Breakfast Passionate Papaya Shake Page..189

Lunch Greek Salad Page..298
Sourdough bread and butter
Celery and carrot sticks
1 banana

Snack 2 slices Zucchini Bread Page..212

Dinner Trout with Almonds Page..245
Potatoes au Gratin Page..343
Sauteed Spinach Page..344
Peach Crumble Page..222

Day 4

Breakfast 1 Cup Oatmeal
1 Cup skim milk
1Cup fresh strawberries

Lunch Chicken Soup Page..322
1 whole wheat roll and butter
Summer Vegetable and
Rice Salad Page..301

Snack 1 banana

Dinner French Beans and
Bay Shrimp Page..157
Coq au Vin Page..284
Brown rice
Glazed Carrots Page..341
Mixed Berry Sherbet Page..221

Day 5

Breakfast	Mocha Shake	Page..187
Lunch	Tuna Sandwich on Rye	Page..308
	Green Salad with	
	Spicy Yogurt Dressing	Page..317
	Banana Cream Pie	Page..201
Snack	1 apple	
Dinner	Babaghanoush	Page..149
	Pita bread	
	Dolmathes	Page..157
	Greek Salad	Page..297
	Lemon Sherbet	Page..220

Day 6

Breakfast	Black Forest Shake	Page..180
Lunch	Chef's Salad	Page..293
	2 slices Soda Bread	
	and butter	Page..210
Snack	1 orange	
Dinner	Corn and Tuna Bisque	Page..323
	Green Salad with Low-Fat	
	Oriental Dressing	Page..314
	Monkfish, Mushrooms	
	and Lentils	Page..235
	Brown Rice	
	Peach Crumble	Page..222

Day 7

Breakfast	Apple Pie Shake	Page..179
Lunch	Pasta Primavera	Page..271
	Green Salad with	
	Vinaigrette Dressing	Page..318
	Italian bread with olive oil	
Snack	1 small bunch grapes	
Dinner	Root Vegetable Soup	Page..331
	1 whole wheat dinner roll	
	Seafood Crepes with	
	Roasted Tomato Sauce	Page..239-241
	MixedSalad with	
	Spicy Yogurt Dressing	Page..317
	Fresh Fruit Salad	Page..217

Chapter Two

The Herbalife Kitchen

- Layout and mood

- Selecting utensils and appliances

- Importance of hygiene

- The well-stocked pantry

- The well-stocked refrigerator

- Cooking methods

- Glossary of terms used in recipes

THE HERBALIFE KITCHEN

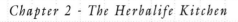

The Herbalife Kitchen is a place to enjoy spending time in creating wonderful recipes and sharing with family and friends. It should not only look clean but be a safe and hygienic environment. A neat and uncluttered environment is the most pleasant and the easiest one for preparing and enjoying good food.

■ GENERAL LAYOUT

Few of us have the luxury of planning and building a new kitchen but if you are fortunate enough to do so, here are some tips. The ideal layout contains a central island with a durable work surface. The appliances are laid out around the walls with a kitchen sink under a window. If there is a dining area in the kitchen it is usually set off to one side. It is handy to have a seating area close by the working area. If the area available is small, then the counters will be set around the wall with no central island or dining area.

The coloring of the room is a personal choice; however, when selecting your design scheme, think of what time of day you will spend most of your time in the kitchen. If it is mostly during the daylight hours, you may want to choose a different shade than if it is more frequently at night.

Choose a floor type that is easy to walk on. Wood or linoleum is more comfortable than ceramic tiles. Ease of cleaning is another factor to look for. If you choose wood, I recommend that it is finished with a high gloss varnish.

Depending upon how much money you have to spend, select from the following lists those items that you feel are essential and that you like. Many appliances are already built in and you don't have much choice; however, if you do purchase your own, always look for the best quality you can afford. Self-cleaning ovens are definitely worth the extra money as are self-defrosting refrigerator/freezers. Select from the following list those items most useful for you.

Major Appliances

1 double oven
1 stove top
1 microwave oven
1 dishwasher
1 refrigerator/freezer

Other Appliances

1 toaster/oven
1 blender
1 electric mixer
1 electric can opener
1 automatic drip coffee maker

UTENSILS

It is a good idea to organize utensils in the following way:

1) Place those most-used hand utensils in a wide-mouth, attractive china jar. This should be located next to the stove top and by a working surface.

2) Place all other hand utensils in a drawer, or drawers, located under a working surface.

3) Larger utensils can be located under other working surfaces where available.

Here is my list of utensils for the Good Kitchen. Select those you find most useful for your lifestyle and eating habits.

Knives

1 large chef's knife (12" heavy blade)
1 small chef's knife (6-8" heavy blade)
1 paring knife (2-4" blade)
1 palette knife or spatula
1 bread knife with serrated blade
1 small serrated blade knife (for slicing tomatoes)
1 grapefruit knife
1 knife sharpener

Spoons

1 large, heavy-duty wooden spoon
1 smaller long-handled wooden spoon
1 slotted spoon
1 ladle
1 stainless steel spatula
1 plastic spatula for nonstick pans
1 set of measuring spoons

Pots and Pans

3 heavy-duty stainless steel saucepans (3, 2 and 1 quart)
(preferably with coated copper base)
2 skillets (non-stick)
1 large size (8 quart) soup or pasta pot
1 heavy oven casserole with lid

Other Utensils

1 balance scale (digital ones are good)
1 large, soft brush for pastry coating
1 bottle opener (hand-held)
1 can opener
1 four-sided stainless steel grater
1 cheese or parsley grater (rotary)
1 garlic press
1 wire whisk
1 juicer (small, hand type)
1 funnel
1 rubber spatula or bowl scraper
1 set of measuring cups
1 glass measuring pitcher
1 pair of kitchen scissors
1 potato peeler
1 potato masher
1 corkscrew
1 peppermill
1 set of tongs
1 bulb baster
1 ice cream scoop
1 wooden rolling pin
1 meat pounder
1 wooden cutting board
1 kitchen timer
2 sets of pot holders (flat and oven mitt style)
2 aprons
2 or more hand towels
2 or more kitchen towels
1 baker's rack
1 set of mixing bowls (5 quarts down to 1 quart)
1 large (8 quart) mixing bowl

2 strainers, large coarse and small fine types
1 colander
aluminum foil
plastic wrap (microwave type and thinner type)
plastic bags (sandwich type)
paper towels on holder

THE IMPORTANCE OF HYGIENE IN THE KITCHEN

Although hygiene is an obvious requirement for the Good Kitchen, it cannot be emphasized often enough. The word hygiene derives from the Greek for healthy; in other words, free of contamination. Contamination can arise from bacteria, viruses or parasites that thrive on food and dirt. Contaminated food often smells and tastes fine which is why every year there are some 9,000 deaths due to food borne illness in the US. Those most at risk are the elderly, infants and those with compromised immune systems. You want to be certain that your kitchen and preparation of food does not lead to contaminated food or food preparation surfaces.

Keep the kitchen clean by using proprietary cleansers. Run any sponges and brushes through with each dishwasher cycle and throw them away after 2 weeks. A spotless-looking kitchen may be contaminated if the sponge you clean with is spreading germs from place to place. Regular wiping down of food preparation surfaces with diluted bleach (1 Tablespoon in 1 Cup of water) is a wise precaution. Here are some tips to prevent food-borne illness:

1) Always thaw frozen meat in the refrigerator, never at room temperature. You may use a microwave or rapid defroster but remember, once defrosted it is vulnerable to contamination.

2) Never leave poultry or meat at room temperature for more than 20 minutes.

3) Cook fish and poultry thoroughly. Use a meat thermometer to be sure.

4) Avoid eating raw or undercooked eggs as these may contain salmonella.

5) Never keep foods warm (temperatures below 140° F) for more than 1 hour.

6) If you have a cut or open place on your skin you MUST cover it well, preferably with a latex glove.

7) Use shallow dishes to distribute heat evenly and cool rapidly.

8) "When in doubt, throw it out."

9) Put perishable goods (fresh fish, meats, frozen and refrigerated goods) away as quickly as possible after purchase. Select frozen foods last when shopping (see Chapter Three), go home right away afterwards and avoid leaving food in a hot car. Never refreeze frozen meat unless it has been cooked in between.

10) Always keep kitchen utensils and preparation surfaces scrupulously clean. Scrub wooden chopping boards after use with salt and a little cool water. Use diluted bleach or a germicide on other surfaces. Clean can openers after each use.

11) Never mix cooked and raw foods together. A common cause of food poisoning is barbecuing meat or chicken and then returning the cooked pieces to the dish they were marinated in. Keep all cooked and raw foods separate in the refrigerator

12) Never use the same knife, spoon or other utensil to mix cooked and raw foods. Up to four million cases of food poisoning are estimated to occur each year; most go unreported. Be sure that you are not the cause of one such incident.

FOOD STORAGE TIPS

See pages 113 through 127 for storage of meat and fish. For fruits, vegetables and grains see each appropriate section in the shopping guide that follows. In general, store perishable goods in the refrigerator and all other goods in a clean, dark and dry place. Bacteria and molds need moisture and warmth to grow so we need to deprive them of these.

- Place items in air-tight packaging (except root vegetables like potatoes, carrots, onions and garlic).
- Use appropriate storage places in the refrigerator.
- Rotate foods regularly.

THE WELL STOCKED PANTRY

Certain items need to be on hand in the Good Kitchen. These have good shelf stability and can be used for unplanned guests, emergencies and other situations. Purchase those items you like and that suit your lifestyle needs.

Standard supplies

Soups and bouillon cubes
Tomato soup
Chicken bouillon cube
Vegetarian bouillon cube

Canned vegetables
Beans, baked
Beans, red kidney in water
Corn (in water)
Tomatoes, plum (large size)
Tomato paste (small size)
Tomato juice
Mushrooms (in water)

Canned meat
Ham
Chicken

Pasta and rice
Spaghetti
Noodles
Brown rice (instant type)
White rice (instant type)

Legumes
White beans
Red kidney beans

Miscellaneous
Chocolate, bitter, cooking slab type
Olive oil
Olive oil spray
Vinegars (rice, white wine, balsamic)
Mayonnaise
Mustard
Olives
Parmesan cheese (in drum package)
Pickles
Relishes
Soy sauce
Vanilla extract

Items for Regular Use

Flour, white, all purpose, unbleached
Flour, whole wheat, stone ground (small packet)
Rolled oats
Bread crumbs
Wheat germ (refrigerate once opened)
Baking powder
Corn starch
Baking yeast
Gelatin, unflavored

Dry seasonings:

Allspice
Basil
Bay leaves
Caraway seeds
Cardamom
Cayenne pepper
Celery seed
Chili powder
Cinnamon (ground and stick)
Cloves (ground and whole)
Coriander
Cream of tartar
Cumin, ground
Curry powder
Dill weed
Ginger, ground
Mace
Marjoram
Mint
Mustard powder
Nutmeg

Oregano
Paprika
Pepper, white, ground
Peppercorns, black
Rosemary
Saffron
Sage
Salt, sea salt
Salt, regular
Savory
Seasoning mixes, e.g. Italian, Mrs. Dash, Vegelite
Tarragon
Turmeric

Perishable Goods For Ongoing Use

Bread
Butter
Cheese
Eggs
Milk
Yogurt
Fresh fruit (including lemons)
Fresh vegetables (including onions, potatoes)

You will have your own additions to these lists but here is a start in creating and finessing your own Good Pantry. Remember to rotate items regularly. Annually spring clean, throwing away items that have been in your pantry longer than two years for dried spices and one year for other less perishable items. Your refrigerator needs to be cleaned and items rotated each week. Clean with a weak solution (½ Teaspoon per 1 Cup) of bicarbonate of soda. Do not use detergents or bleach inside a refrigerator.

HEALTHY COOKING

So, now you have a well equipped kitchen - what do you do in it? Prepare healthy meals of course! Preparing and cooking food is not as difficult as it may sound. The Herbalife way of good eating is lower in animal fat and higher in botanical factors. Here are some ways to achieve this using your favorite recipes:

To Reduce **FAT** in the recipe

- place chopped onions in the microwave in a small amount of chicken stock instead of sautéing in butter or oil on top of the stove.
- crisp tortilla chips in the microwave instead of frying them in oil.
- substitute apple, apricot or prune puree in place of some butter in sweet recipes.

To Reduce **SUGAR** in the recipe

- substitute 1 Cup of sugar with ¾ Cup of honey and a pinch of baking soda. Reduce the liquid by ¼ Cup.
- substitute 1 Cup of sugar with 1 ¼ Cups of molasses and ½ teaspoon of baking soda. Reduce the liquid of the recipe by 5 Tablespoons.

Never substitute more than ½ of the solid sugar in a recipe with a liquid one.

Recipes often use terms that you may not be familiar with. See pages 59 through 65 for a glossary of terms to help you carry out the instructions and achieve a perfect result.

FOOD MEASURING

A vital part of all food preparation is accurate weighing and measuring of food. Recipes are only reproducible if you measure accurately. Here are some tips:

1) Use standardized measuring pitchers or spoons.
2) Measure dry ingredients like flour, sugar or herbs by spooning into the measuring utensil rather than removing directly from the package.
3) Add to just above the level of

a measuring cup and level using the straight edge of a knife.

4) For precision, measure over paper or foil, not over the mixing bowl.

5) Do not pack down dry goods except brown sugar.

6) Lower yourself to the eye level of a liquid to measure rather than raising the cup or pitcher to your eye level.

7) Spray a measuring cup with a little oil to avoid honey or peanut butter from sticking.

- Wipe mushrooms with a damp cloth.
- Wash all fruit well with a little bleach (1 teaspoon per gallon of water) and rinse again. This will remove any surface bacteria.
- Wipe all meat with a paper towel. You may wipe the surface with a little vinegar for extra cleanliness.
- Wipe all fish with a paper towel.
- Use a separate spoon to remove dry goods before measuring. Always use clean utensils for each ingredient.

FOOD PREPARATION METHODS

Cleaning, Scrubbing, Peeling

Most vegetables require washing and removal of the outer layers. New carrots or potatoes may be scrubbed with a small brush and the skin left on. As most of the minerals are to be found just under the skin, remove only the very outermost layers using a special peeler rather than a knife. An exception is potato that has turned green due to exposure to light in the soil. This needs to be completely removed with a knife as it is toxic. All mold, rot or fungus on root vegetables should be completely removed also.

COOKING METHODS

1) Moist Methods

Steaming, Sautéing and Stewing This way the natural flavors and juices are retained and is especially well-suited to tougher cuts of meat. Stewing is usually preceded by quickly sealing the juices into the meat by sautéing first before the liquid is added.

2) Dry Methods

Frying, Roasting, Broiling

3) Microwaving

4) Pressure Cooking

Here is a list of cooking terms and methods used in most recipes. We have kept the preparation of the recipes in this book as simple as possible. An important ingredient for a successful meal is to plan ahead. Make a list of the ingredients you need to purchase for the recipe, get your utensils ready ahead of time and follow the directions carefully.

The overall impression and experience of the Good Kitchen should be one of pleasant efficiency. Enjoy yours.

GOOD COOKING METHODS AND PROCEDURES

BAKE is to cook by dry heat. Free circulation of air is important, so items should not be crowded in the oven. Ovens should be preheated for 10 to 15 minutes, and the temperature checked with a thermometer.

OVEN TEMPERATURES:

250 ° F	very slow
300 ° F	slow
325 ° F	moderately slow
350 ° F	moderate
375 ° F	moderately hot
400 ° F	hot
450-500 ° F	very hot

BARBECUE involves cooking on a grill over intense heat, usually a charcoal or wood fire.

BASTE is to brush on or pour liquid over foods while cooking in order to moisten them and add flavor. Use a brush, bulb baster or spoon.

BEAT is to mix ingredients rapidly to make a mixture smooth and light by incorporating air into it. Beating is done with an electric mixer or by hand using a whisk, fork or wooden spoon.

BIND is to thicken ingredients and cause them to form a cohesive mass by adding a binding agent such as beaten egg, gelatin, flour or bread crumbs.

HELP! What to do if you overseason.

1) Add a peeled, whole raw potato to absorb the flavor. Remove before serving.
2) Serve the dish chilled as the cold temperature will blunt the flavor.
3) Add more bland ingredients like potato, flour or corn flour to absorb the flavor.

BLANCH is to cook briefly in boiling water. Blanching is done for various reasons: to begin the cooking process; to help in the loosening and removal of peels or shells (tomatoes, almonds); to enhance color and reduce bitterness (raw vegetables); to seal in juices or remove strong flavors (such as excess salt from meats such as bacon); to destroy harmful enzymes and extend storage life when freezing or canning (raw vegetables to be frozen). Many foods, such as vegetables, can be blanched either with water or with steam (which conserves nutrients). Steam-blanching may be done in a pot with a steaming rack or in the microwave.

BLEND involves incorporating two or more ingredients by hand or with an electric mixer until smooth or until they combine to produce uniform texture, flavor or color.

BOIL is to heat a liquid until it is in motion and bubbles break continually on the surface. At sea level, boiling point is 212 ° F (100 ° C). It is higher at high altitudes.

BONE is to separate the flesh off fish, poultry and meat from the bones.

BRAISE is to cook slowly, covered, in a small amount of liquid, usually on a bed of chopped aromatic vegetables. Braising helps tenderize fibrous vegetables and tough cuts of meat. Generally, a quarter to a half inch of liquid is added to the bottom of the pot in which the food is being braised, and the pot is tightly covered to prevent evaporation. Braising can be done in the oven or on top of the stove.

BROIL is to cook under strong, direct heat. If done properly, broiling food browns the surface while cooking the interior to taste. Foods are usually placed four to six inches from the heat source. Distance from the heat source is crucial in maintaining a balance between rapid surface cooking and slower internal cooking. Generally, the larger the food item, the longer its broiling time, and thus the farther it should be placed from the heat source.

BROWN involves deepening the surface color of foods by exposing them to high temperatures. Browning may be done under a broiler, in fat on top of the stove or in the oven.

BRUISE is to partially crush food (such as peppercorns and garlic cloves) in order to release flavor. Bruising is done with the heel of a knife or with a mortar and pestle.

BUTTERFLY is to halve food horizontally without cutting all the way through it so that the two halves can be pulled open and spread out.

CANDY means to coat with sugar or to preserve or glaze by cooking in sugary syrup.

CARAMELIZE is to heat sugar slowly until it melts and turns brown.

CHOP is to cut food into pieces with a knife or other device.

CLARIFY is to separate and remove impurities from a liquid such as butter or stock, thereby making it clear. Clarify butter by melting it, then skimming off the surface foam and discarding the milk solids which have settled to the bottom. To clarify stock, add egg whites to warm stock. The egg whites will coagulate and rise to the surface, trapping impurities floating in the stock as they rise. Then skim and strain the liquid.

CODDLE is to poach gently in barely simmering water.

CREAM is to beat one or more foods together until soft, smooth and blended.

CRIMP is to make a decorative edge along a pie or pastry by pinching with a fork, pastry crimper or your fingers.

CURE means to preserve foods, especially meats and fish, by salting and/or smoking.

CUT IN means to incorporate solid fat and dry ingredients with a cutting motion until the mixture coarsens. Use two knives, a pastry blender, a fork or your fingers.

DEEP-FRY is to cook foods in deep, hot fat or oil. The quality and temperature of the oil as well as the coating on the food are important to good frying. The best oil for frying is a clear, mild vegetable oil that can withstand high temperatures without smoking or burning. The oil should be between 360° F and 390° F for best results. At this temperature, the batter or coating will absorb the minimal amount of oil. Oil that is too hot will burn the food. The oil itself will begin to burn when it reaches 400° F. If the oil is too cool, the food will absorb a lot of oil before it is fully cooked.

DEGLAZE is to remove and preserve the natural glaze that accumulates in a cooking pan by pouring liquid into the pan in which food has been cooked, scraping up the brown, crusty bits that form on the bottom.

DEGREASE is to remove grease from soups, stocks, gravies and sauces by skimming fat off of the top.

DEVEIN is to remove the black intestinal vein that runs along the outside of a shrimp. Slit the shrimp along the back and pull away the vein.

DICE is to cut food into tiny, even cubes.

DREDGE is to coat food with dry ingredients such as flour or sugar. This can be done by sprinkling the powdery substance over the food, dragging the food through the powdery substance or by shaking the two together in a bag.

EVISCERATE is to remove the internal organs of animals, birds or fish in preparation for cooking.

FILLET is to remove the bones from meat or fish.

FLAMBÉ is to ignite foods that have some form of potable alcohol, e.g., cognac added for dramatic effect and to develop a rich flavor.

FOLD, FOLD IN is to incorporate a light, aerated substance such as whipped cream or beaten egg whites into a heavier substance without deflating the lighter mixture. Use your hands, a rubber spatula or a spoon. Cut through and turn over, rotating the bowl.

FRICASSÉE is to stew gently in liquid and aromatic vegetables.

GLAZE is to coat a surface with a thin layer of a substance in order to give it a shiny finish.

GRATE involves reducing food to tiny particles, flakes or shreds by rubbing it against a grater or using a food processor.

GRILL is to cook food over a grid of metal bars set over an intense heat source such as charcoal, wood, electricity or gas.

GRIND is to reduce foods to tiny particles either mechanically or by hand.

JULIENNE is to cut into thin strips.

KNEAD is to work dough, either by hand or mechanically, into a smooth and malleable mass to develop the gluten in the flour. Gluten gives structure to the baked product.

MACERATE is to place fruits in a flavored liquid such as sugar and lemon, wine or a liqueur and let them stand to improve flavor and soften texture.

MARINATE is to cover foods with a wet or dry mixture in order to tenderize and infuse flavor. Wet marinades generally contain an acid which aids in the tenderization. Dry marinades consist of herbs and spices.

MICROWAVE is to cook foods in a microwave oven. This method is fast, clean and cool. Many foods cook in a fourth of the time and with less energy than they would in a conventional oven or on a surface cooking unit. Microwaves are short, high-frequency radio waves. They are attracted to molecules in sugar, fat and water only and will not penetrate metal. Microwaves cook food from the outside in. Microwave ovens do not brown foods or produce a crisp crust. Steaming or moist-heat cooking is what the microwave does best.

MINCE is to chop very finely.

PAN-BROIL is to cook in a frying pan, using little or no fat, over moderately hot heat.

PAN-FRY is to cook food in a frying pan in a small amount of hot fat.

PARBOIL is to partially cook foods in boiling water.

PARE is to remove the outer skin of fruits and vegetables with a peeler or small paring knife.

PEEL is to remove the skin of a fruit or vegetable. Sometimes briefly heating the food makes peeling easier.

PICKLE is to preserve meats, vegetables and fruits in seasoned brine.

PLUMP is to soak dried fruits in liquid until they swell.

POACH is to cook food gently in simmering liquid.

PUREE is to mash, blend, sieve or process food into a smooth, soft consistency.

REDUCE means to boil down a liquid rapidly to decrease the volume and intensify flavors.

REFRESH is to plunge boiled foods into cold water immediately after cooking to stop it from cooking further, to set color and crisp texture.

RICE is to force cooked root vegetables through a ricer which breaks the vegetable up into particles that look like grains of rice.

ROAST is to cook food by dry heat in an oven. Roasting is the same as baking but often includes basting.

SAUTÉ is to cook in a pan on top of the stove with a small quantity of oil. In order to sauté successfully, the fat must be hot enough, the food must be dry when it is added to the pan and the pan must not be too crowded. Oil or a combination of oil and butter are best for sautéing. This method is also like stir frying.

SCALD milk means to heat it until tiny bubbles form around the inside edge of the pan but the milk is not quite boiling. To scald solid food means to briefly drop it into boiling water or pour boiling water over it.

SCORE means to make shallow cuts, usually in a crisscross pattern, through the top layer of meats and fish to tenderize them or of dough to decorate baked products.

SEAR means to subject meat to intense heat in order to brown the meat and seal in the juices. Searing can be done in a skillet on top of the stove or in the oven.

SIMMER means to boil gently so that the liquid barely bubbles.

STEAM means to cook food with steam heat which is intense, moist heat. Food is placed above, but not in, boiling liquid and the steam circulates around the food. The cooking container is sealed to prevent the steam from escaping. Steaming is a much wiser cooking method in terms of nutrition than boiling as there is less loss of water-soluble vitamins. In order to steam successfully, steam must be able to circulate freely in the steamer; the food being steamed should never touch the boiling liquid; and there must be sufficient liquid so that it does not boil dry. Microwave ovens are excellent for steaming. Food may also be steamed enfolded in foil in a conventional oven.

STEW is to cook slowly in liquid for a long period of time over low heat.

STIR-FRY is to cook small pieces of meat and vegetables quickly over high heat in a small amount of oil. Stir-frying is very similar to sautéing. Stir-fried foods are cooked by both the heat of the oil and the heat of the pan, and the ingredients are stirred almost constantly so that they cook evenly. Stir-frying is a good cooking method for preserving nutrients, colors, textures and flavors of foods. This method is similar to sautéing.

TRUSS means to bind the appendages of a bird close to the body so that it will keep its shape during cooking.

WHIP means to beat a mixture rapidly in a circular motion thereby incorporating air into it. This lightens and increases the volume of the mixture. Whipping is done with a whisk, electric mixer or rotary beater.

WHISK means to beat with a whisk until well mixed.

Chapter Three

The Herbalife Good Food Shopper

- Where and when to shop for food

- Reading food labels

- Selecting foods as:

    - Items for long-term backup storage

    - Items for shorter-term backup storage

- Selecting fruits and vegetables; culinary herbs and spices; fish, meats and poultry; cheese; grains and beans

THE HERBALIFE GOOD FOOD SHOPPER

Few people today have the opportunity to grow their own fruits or vegetables, let alone grain. Most of us depend upon an agricultural system that brings these items as well as meats, poultry and fish to our local store. Farmers' Markets are one way to purchase produce fresher than usual because they come direct from the grower. Below is a guide for the discerning food shopper.

We suggest that you have two main sources for foods:

A) a less expensive large supermarket type of store for weekly supplies and

B) a gourmet type of store for special events and dinner parties.

For regular supermarket shopping here are some suggestions:

1) Make a list. Make this available in your kitchen for spontaneous additions by yourself and other members of the family. Place it on the refrigerator or on a bulletin board nearby.

2) Create weekly menus. Post the menus for the family to see and make changes to if they wish.

3) Choose a day to shop that is **a)** convenient to your schedule and budget and **b)** close to when fresh produce is delivered to your market. Find out when this is from your local market's manager.

4) Learn how to read labels. Recognize misleading packaging or claims. Recent legislation has improved the situation.

GOOD FOOD LABEL READING

There are two main areas of a label to be aware of:
1) The Nutrition label
2) The Ingredient label

Nutrition Facts

Serving Size 3 Tablespoons (29 g)
Servings Per Container 19

Amount Per Serving	Powder	Powder with 8 fl. oz. nonfat milk
Calories	100	190
Calories from Fat	5	10

	% Daily Value**	
Total Fat 0.5 g*	1%	2%
Saturated Fat 0 g	0%	0%
Cholesterol less than 5 mg	1%	2%
Sodium 80 mg	3%	8%
Potassium 210 mg	6%	18%
Total Carbohydrate 18 g	6%	10%
Dietary Fiber 2 g	8%	8%
Sugars 15 g		
Protein 8 g	16%	32%

Vitamin A	25%	35%
Vitamin C	25%	30%
Calcium	15%	45%
Iron	25%	25%
Vitamin D	25%	50%
Vitamin E	25%	25%
Thiamin	25%	30%
Riboflavin	25%	45%
Niacin	25%	25%
Vitamin B6	25%	30%
Folate	0%	4%
Vitamin B12	25%	40%
Biotin	25%	25%
Pantothenic Acid	25%	35%
Phosphorus	15%	40%
Magnesium	10%	20%
Zinc	25%	30%
Copper	25%	25%

* Amount in Powder. One cup Vitamin A & D fortified nonfat milk contributes an additional 90 calories, 5 calories from fat, 0.4 g fat, 0.3 g saturated fat, 4 mg cholesterol, 126 mg sodium, 406 mg potassium, 12 g total carbohydrate (12 g sugars), and 8 g protein.

** Percent Daily Values are based on a 2000 calorie diet. Your daily values may be higher or lower depending on your calorie needs.

	Calories	2,000	2,500
Total Fat	Less Than	65 g	80 g
Sat. Fat	Less Than	20 g	25 g
Cholesterol	Less Than	300 mg	300 mg
Sodium	Less Than	2,400 mg	2,400 mg
Potassium		3,500 mg	3,500 mg
Total Carbohydrate		300 g	375 g
Dietary Fiber		25 g	30 g
Protein		50 g	65 g

Ingredients: Fructose, nonfat dry milk, calcium sodium caseinate, corn bran fiber, powdered cellulose, natural and artificial flavors, guar gum, casein, soy lecithin, canola oil, oat fiber, carrageenan, potassium chloride, medium chain triglycerides, fructooligosaccharides, magnesium oxide, dicalcium phosphate, psyllium husk, Aminogen®†, citrus pectin, honey powder, ginger root, ascorbic acid, vitamin E acetate, ferrous fumarate, licorice root, hawthorne berry, gotu kola, dandelion root, parsley, papaya, Yellow 5 and Yellow 6, niacinamide, zinc oxide, copper gluconate, vitamin A palmitate, calcium pantothenate, papain, bromelain, pyridoxine hydrochloride, thiamin mononitrate, riboflavin, vitamin D3, biotin and cyanocobalamin.

Formulated exclusively for:
HERBALIFE INTERNATIONAL
Los Angeles, CA 90080-0210, U.S.A.
MADE IN U.S.A.

* This label does not represent the actual size.

The ingredient label lists the ingredients in descending order by weight. Note that sweeteners are often listed separately to avoid looking as though the item contains a lot of sugar (which is rarely listed as such). The following are common names for sweeteners: brown sugar, corn syrup, high fructose corn sweetener, honey, malt or maltodextrin, dextrose or any other item ending in "ose". New requirements for sublisting of items like cheese or mayonnaise now exist so cheese may read cheese (milk, culture, enzymes) and mayonnaise (soy oil, egg yolk, lemon juice) which is more informative than previously. Furthermore, it enables you to identify food colorants or sulfites you may be sensitive to.

The nutrition label has received attention recently due to a tightening and change in the labeling laws which was completed by May of 1994. Before this date, the food industry voluntarily complied with rather fuzzy guidelines. Today, the labeling is mandatory and regulated by the FDA. A recent survey showed that industry compliance is very high and most people feel that there has been a significant improvement in the way information is presented on food packaging. Below is a typical template for an FDA approved label on a packet over 40 square inches in size (smaller packets may omit some of this information).

The first noticeable difference compared with older labels is the format itself. The new labels are entitled NUTRITION FACTS and the information is divided by two large bold lines and one narrower bold line beginning with the serving size which is now standardized so that a direct comparison of similar items can be made. Earlier, for example, one box of crackers might list a serving size of 10 crackers weighing 1½oz. and another manufacturer of a similar product would list eight crackers weighing one oz. You had to be a real mathematician to figure out a comparison before, but now it is much easier. The serving size is standardized and must be reasonable. For instance, previously a salad dressing could say a serving was one tablespoon which was pretty unlikely whereas now it must be a standard two tablespoons for all dressings and sauces. Underneath the serving size is listed how many servings are in each container.

Energy

Next comes the information about each serving within the container beginning with the amount of calories (energy) provided and how many of these calories come from fat. Below this information is listed the total fat in grams and to the right this is expressed as the percentage of the Daily Value (using 2,000 and 2,500 calories daily intake as a guide). The Daily Value is a new term used to describe how many calories an average woman and an average man respectively consumes per day. Below this section, on packaging that is sufficiently large, there is an expansion of this concept to list the values for each Daily Value, for 2,000 calories per day and for 2,500 calories per day intake. On smaller packages this information is omitted.

Fat and Cholesterol

The fat content is subdivided so that the saturated fat and cholesterol is also listed because of the health risks attached to a diet proportionately high in these. Recent understanding of the value of omega-3 fatty acids is not covered by this legislation however, you may see these listed here in the future on the label.

Sodium

Under the Cholesterol value is listed Sodium. This is important information for those with high blood pressure who may be sodium (or salt) sensitive. Sodium chloride is the technical name for table salt but sodium appears in many other forms in processed food. Since a lot of sodium is in processed foods, those on a sodium restricted diet should check carefully.

Carbohydrate

The way carbohydrate is presented is new and different for most consumers. Now the label lists total carbohydrate first and then subdivides this number into *unavailable*, also called dietary fiber, and *available* as starch and sugars. Most Americans consume too much sugar and not enough dietary fiber. This information can help guide the consumer and is more helpful than just total carbohydrate information. There is no reference value for sugar so the right hand column next to sugars is empty.

Protein

The last item on this section of the label is the protein content. This is listed in grams and is not related to the % Daily Reference Value because this varies according to body size. (See Chapter One, page 20).

Micronutrients

The next section of the label relates to micronutrients. The way they are expressed is as a percentage of the total daily intake (Reference Daily Intake or RDI). Unless the consumer knows the RDI for these nutrients, they cannot know exactly how much is in the product using this method. Daily Reference Value and Reference Daily Intake are food industry terms used for labeling.

Vitamins

Vitamins A and C are now listed whereas earlier voluntary labeling used to also list the B vitamins. The scientific consensus is that due to fortification of wheat flour with B vitamins, this information is no longer mandatory but at the discretion of the food manufacturer. Not all nutritionists agree that Americans receive sufficient B vitamins in their food, particularly folacin (also called folate or folic acid), to justify omitting this information, but it is easier to see a label containing only two vitamins instead of eight or ten. Vitamin A in a vegetarian product comes from beta carotene (Retinol Equivalent) but if it is from an animal (or fish) source then it is in the form of retinol. The Reference Daily Intake (RDI) for Vitamin A is 875 Retinol Equivalents (RE) (computed from the forms of Vitamin A that provide biological activity). The International Units (IU) nomenclature is no longer used.

Vitamin C is expressed as a percentage of the RDI (60 milligrams per day). Again, not every nutritionist agrees that this is sufficiently high to offset increased requirements due to environmental pollution, smoking and other pro-oxidants.

Minerals

The minerals calcium and iron are also listed on the micronutrient portion of the food label. Previously, zinc and other minerals were listed which made for lengthy and difficult-to-read labels. The RDI of calcium is 800 milligrams per day and the label expresses the percentage of calcium in the food per serving which is lower than the US Recommended Daily Allowance (RDA) of 1000 milligrams. The RDA is scaled to different age groups whereas the RDI is a general recommendation for the whole population. The RDI for iron is 12 milligrams for food labeling purposes which is lower than the RDA for women of 18 milligrams for the same reason.

Reference Percent Daily Value

The Reference Percent Daily Value is also computed using the RDI concept rather than the RDA. There are two energy intakes expressed: 2000 calories and 2500 calories. Many dieters or sedentary people consume less than 2000 calories but this is a general reference guide that is workable for most people.

I have described these new labels in detail because I believe that the good food shopper needs to understand what they do and don't convey.

Daily Reference Values (DRV) Used in Food Labeling in Nutrition Facts

Food Component ....DRV
Total fat ....75 grams
Saturated fat ....25 grams
Unsaturated fat ....50 grams
Cholesterol ....300 milligrams
Total carbohydrates ....325 grams
Dietary fiber ....25 grams
Sodium ....2,400 milligrams
Potassium ....3,500 milligrams

Recommended Daily Intakes (RDI) used in Food Labeling in Nutrition Facts

	Good Source	Excellent Source
Vitamin A	8 RE	16 RE
Vitamin C	6 mg	12 mg
Vitamin B6	0.15 mg	0.30 mg
Vitamin B12	0.2 mcg	0.4 mcg
Vitamin B1	0.12 mg	0.24 mg
Folacin	18 mcg	36 mcg
Niacin	1.6 mg	3.2 mg
Calcium	90 mg	180 mg
Iron	1.2 mg	2.4 mg
Zinc	1.3 mg	2.6 mg

NEW FOOD LABELING SUMMARY

(Enforced May, 1994)

Benefits	Drawbacks
Total fat listed in grams.	Not identified as percentage of calories coming from fat.
Saturated fat listed separately.	Polyunsaturated fat nor monounsaturates not listed.
Dietary fiber listed.	Soluble and insoluble are not separated. Soluble helps with cholesterol balance. Insoluble is more important for maintaining healthy colon bacteria and reducing constipation.
Vitamin A listed in Retinol Equivalents.	Beta carotene not listed. Some people are not familiar with the concept of Vitamin A activity. Other carotenoids that may have antioxidant activity not included.
Clearer label with no B vitamins listed.	No folacin listed. (important information for young, child-bearing age women to avoid risk of neural tube defect infants)

The rest of the information presented on a food label is also regulated by the Food and Drug Administration so that no false or misleading claims may be made. You will no longer read "peanut butter no cholesterol" or "baked potato chips" or other claims implying low fat that are not in reality. Here is a guide to what you will see and what it means.

GLOSSARY OF TERMS USED IN FOOD LABELING

FREE

Calorie Free - 5 or less calories per serving.

Fat Free/Nonfat

0.5 grams of fat or less per serving.

Cholesterol Free

2 milligrams or less per serving.

Sodium Free

5 milligrams or less per serving.

Sugar Free

0.5 grams or less per serving.

LOW

Low Calorie

40 calories or less for foods.
120 calories or less for meals.

Low Sodium

140 milligrams or less per serving.

Low Fat

3 grams or less for foods.
30% or less fat calories for meals.

Low Saturated Fat

1 gram or less and
15% or less for foods.
10% or less for meals.
Cholesterol 20 milligrams or less.

REDUCED/LESS/FEWER

Calories
25% reduction compared with reference food.

Sodium
25% reduction compared with reference food.

Total Fat
25% reduction compared with reference food.

Saturated Fat
25% reduction compared with reference food.

Cholesterol
25% reduction compared with reference food.

Sugars
25% reduction compared with reference food.

OTHER CLAIMS

Calories
"Lite" if 1/3 less or 50% less fat calories.

Sodium
"Very Low Sodium" is 35 milligrams or less.
"Light Sodium" is 50% or less.
"Lightly Salted" is 50% or less added sodium.
"Salt Free" is "Sodium Free"

Total Fat
"Lite" is 50% or less fat.
"Fat Free" means no added fat and less than 0.5 grams of fat per serving.
"Lean" is less than 10 grams of fat and less than 4 grams of saturated fat and less than 95 milligrams of cholesterol per serving.
"Extra Lean" is less than 5 grams of fat and less than 2 grams of saturated fat and less than 95 milligrams of cholesterol per serving.

Sugars
"No Sugar Added".

Vitamins and Minerals
"High" is 20% or more of the Daily Value.
"Good Source" is 10-19% of the Daily Value.

Dietary Fiber
"High" is 20% or more of the Daily Value.
"More" is 10% more nutrient than the reference food

Armed with all of this information, you are now ready to go food shopping.

SUPERMARKET LAYOUT

Here is how a typical supermarket is laid out. Your local market may be laid out differently so get to know yours well.

You can see that most markets are designed for you to arrive in the fresh produce section. This is the most colorfully displayed and attractive area of the market. From there you weave your way through the aisles where the non-perishable sections are located and finally around the perimeter where the refrigerated sections are located.

Most people begin with the fresh produce section. Potatoes and other heavy items should go into the cart first. Easily crushed produce should go into the upper compartment. Here is a guide to selecting fresh produce and its seasonality. If your market is laid out so that you begin at the dairy and fresh refrigerated section of the perimeter, then you will end with the fresh produce.

Next, place heavy, non-perishable household goods in your cart. These can usually be found in the first and second aisles where soap, household cleaning products, and paper goods are located. From here you can wind your way to the canned and packaged non-perishable foods and stop at the dairy, meat and fish containers which are usually located around the walls. On pages 113 through 127 we describe how to tell the freshness of meat and fish. The freezers are usually in one or two aisles of a large market and you should go to this section last of all.

If you have small children, carefully select your check out line so that they are not tempted by too much candy. Give them a piece of fruit or a healthy snack as they, too, deserve a reward.

Use the following guides to help you select your food items in the categories of:

- Fruits and vegetables on pages 81-101
- Culinary herbs on pages 102-107
- Culinary spices on pages 107-112
- Fish on pages 113-117
- Meat on pages 117-123
- Poultry and game birds on pages 123-124
- Variety meats on pages 125-126
- Smoked and cured meats on pages 126-127
- Cheese on pages 127-131
- Grains on pages 131-137
- Beans on pages 137-139

Guide to Selecting Produce

Nutritional Rating:

Excellent Source is if a food contains 20% or more of the Recommended Daily Intake (RDI).

Good Source is if a food contains between 10 and 19% of the RDI.

Apples

Availability: Year round, apples are the largest fruit crop grown in temperate climates. More apples are produced in the United States than in any other country in the world. Apples are a member of the rose family and their colors range from green to yellow to red. Harvested late summer to late fall, most varieties store well in winter. Apples are a good source of vitamin A.

How to Select: Choose apples that are bright-skinned, plump and firm to the touch. Avoid rot and bruises because these spread quickly. Shriveled, over-ripe apples can be used to hasten the ripening of other fruits. Punch a few holes in a paper bag and place the ripe apple inside it with other fruit.

Uses: Apples can be eaten raw or they can be poached, stewed, baked, broiled, puréed, fried, sautéed and pressed for brandy and cider. The apple can be a snack, side dish or dessert. Apples work well in salads, tarts, pies, cakes, fritters, preserves, jellies, relishes and mincemeat. Combine with raisins, citrus fruits, sweet spice, brown sugar, pork, chicken, veal, turkey, duck and goose as well as dairy products such as cheese, cream and ice cream.

Storage: Store in the refrigerator for one to two weeks, or in a cool, dark, dry, well-ventilated place for longer periods. Apples left at room temperature for more than a day or two continue to ripen and become soft. Examples: McIntosh, Granny Smith, Red Delicious, Golden Delicious, Rome Beauty.

Nutritional Analysis: one medium apple (4.8 oz) has 80 calories, 13% RDA Vitamin C, less than one gram of fat and is a good source of fiber.

Apricots

Availability: May to August. More than ninety percent of apricots in the United States are grown in California. Apricots are an excellent source of vitamin A.

What to look for: Select fruit that is golden orange with a bit of a blush, plump, sweet-smelling and beginning to soften. Complete the ripening at room temperature. Storage: Store ripe fruit in the refrigerator for up to three weeks.

Guide to Selecting Produce

Nutritional Rating:

Excellent Source is if a food contains 20% or more of the Recommended Daily Intake (RDI).

Good Source is if a food contains between 10 and 19% of the RDI.

Uses: Use apricots in fruit salads. Combine with poultry and game in salads and hot dishes. Use in tarts, pies, preserves, relishes, ice creams and sorbets.

Nutritional Analysis: Three apricots (3.75 oz) have 50 calories, 55% RDA of Vitamin A, 17% RDA Vitamin C, are a good source of Vitamins E and K and have less than one gram of fat.

Artichokes

Availability: Year round. Peak season and lowest prices in the spring.

Artichokes are fun to eat and a delicious, low-calorie source of potassium and vitamins A and C.

What to look for: Choose tightly-headed, compact, heavy, plump, firm green globes with fresh green leaves and stems. Avoid spreading leaves which are a sign of flavor loss and staleness. Avoid softness and blackening or rust, except on cold weather artichokes which may have some darkening on the tips of the leaves without affecting the flavor.

Uses: Artichokes can be steamed, boiled, simmered or microwaved. They can also be stuffed, baked or fried. Both the heart and the ends of the leaves are edible and have a subtle, nutty flavor. Serve artichokes hot or cold with a dipping sauce such as yogurt dip, hollandaise, lemon butter, vinaigrette or mayonnaise. Combine artichokes with vegetables, herbs, cheese, eggs, olive oil, lamb, seafood and chicken.

Storage: Store wrapped in the refrigerator for up to two days.

Nutritional Analysis: One medium artichoke has 60 calories, 10% RDA of Vitamin C, good source of folacin, Vitamins B1 and K, Magnesium, Phosphorus, Niacin and Iron, less than one gram of fat, and is a good source of dietary fiber.

Arugula

Availability: Year round. Prime season is April to October.

Also known as rocket, arugula is a member of the mustard family (a cruciferous vegetable). Its dark green leaves are pungent and spicy.

What to look for: Choose tender, fresh-looking, smallish leaves with a good green color. The larger the leaves the more pungent the flavor.

Uses: Use arugula in salads with more mild lettuces, tomatoes and scallions. Arugula can also be added to hot pasta dishes, soups and stews just before serving. **Storage:** Store in the refrigerator wrapped and unwashed for up to two days. **Nutritional Analysis:** ½ cup has two calories, less than one gram of fat.

Asparagus
Availability: Year round. Prime season for best flavor and lowest price is in the spring. Asparagus comes in both green and white forms. The more expensive white asparagus has been blanched by being covered with soil and has a milder flavor. **What to look for:** Choose straight, plump, crisp bright green stalks with tightly closed tips. **Uses:** Serve asparagus raw, steamed or simmered. Use in salads, stir-fries and combined with any meat. Use the tough bottoms of the stalks to make stocks. **Storage:** Store wrapped in the refrigerator for up to two days. **Nutritional Analysis:** ½ cup has 24 calories, is a good source of Vitamins B1, B2, Folacin, C, E, and K and has less than one gram of fat.

Avocados
Availability: Year round. Peak season is January to May. Haas avocados are small, black and bumpy-skinned. Their flesh has a dense, creamy texture which is richer than that of the larger, green, smooth-skinned Fuerte variety. **What to look for:** Choose firm, fresh-smelling fruit that is free from bruises or cuts and slightly soft to the touch. Rock-hard avocados have been picked too soon and may rot before they ripen. Ripen at room temperature. **Uses:** Use avocados with tomato and onion to make guacamole. Slice into salads combined with sprouts, greens, fresh herbs, onions, chilies, garlic, lemon or lime, tomatoes, chicken or turkey, shellfish and vinaigrette. Stuff avocado halves with egg or seafood salad. Add avocado slices to sandwiches or use as a sandwich spread. Mashed avocado adds a wonderful creaminess to salad dressings. **Storage:** Store ripe avocados in the refrigerator for a few days. **Nutritional Analysis:** ½ avocado (3 oz.) has 153 calories, 10% RDA Vitamin A, 11% RDA Vitamin C, 15 grams of fat, and is a good source of dietary fiber.

Guide to Selecting Produce

Nutritional Rating:

Excellent Source is if a food contains 20% or more of the Recommended Daily Intake (RDI).

Good Source is if a food contains between 10 and 19% of the RDI.

Bananas
Availability: Year round.
What to look for: Select firm, slightly green bananas that are free of blemishes and are still attached to the stem. Bananas that have broken off may not ripen properly. Ripen at room temperature.
Uses: Eat bananas fresh or sliced in fruit salads. Use them in pies, cakes, cookies, breads, puddings, soufflés, fritters, curries, custards, milk shakes and with ice cream. Bananas can be fried, broiled or baked.
Storage: Store at room temperature.
Nutritional Analysis: One medium banana has 105 calories, is a good source of potassium, less than one gram of fat.

Beets
Availability: Year round. Prime season is summer to early fall. The sweetest of vegetables.
What to look for: Choose small to medium-sized beets without bruises or dents and with fresh greens attached. Large beets tend to be woody, stale and less sweet. Beets must have the tapering root end intact and at least one inch of stem still attached or they will lose color, flavor and nutritional value when cooked.
Uses: Beets may be baked, steamed or boiled whole until tender. The skins then slip off and the beets may be flavored with vinegar or orange. They work well in soups such as borscht and in relishes and salads. The green beet tops may be steamed, simmered, sautéed, stir-fried or added to soups and stews.
Storage: To store beets, remove greens and keep wrapped in the refrigerator for a few days.
Nutritional Analysis: ½ Cup has 26 calories, is a good source of folacin, Vitamins C and K, and Magnesium, and has less than one gram of fat per serving.

Broccoli
Availability: Year round. A highly nutritious member of the cruciferous family.
What to look for: Choose crisp broccoli with tight green or purplish-green florets and fresh leaves. Avoid yellowing, flowering or wilt as well as those with thick, woody stalks.
Uses: Broccoli may be eaten raw in salads and with dips. For salads, do not dress the broccoli until just before serving as acid will yellow it. It is also delicious steamed, blanched, stir-fried and added to a variety of dishes.

Guide to Selecting Produce

Nutritional Rating:

Excellent Source is if a food contains 20% or more of the Recommended Daily Intake (RDI).

Good Source is if a food contains between 10 and 19% of the RDI.

Storage: Store wrapped in the refrigerator for a few days.
Nutritional Analysis: One stalk (5.3 oz.) has 30 calories, 10% RDA Vitamin A, 240% RDA Vitamin C, less than one gram of fat and is a good source of dietary fiber.

Brussels Sprouts
Availability: October to March Another member of the cruciferous family.
What to look for: Choose firm, compact sprouts with a bright green color and of the smallest size available. Avoid wilt and yellowing.
Uses: Prepare brussels sprouts by steaming, simmering, sautéing or stir-frying. Cook for only the minimum amount of time required in order for the sprouts to retain a crisp center, bright green color and nutrient value. Season with lemon, nuts, water chestnuts or poppy seeds. Use in salads, casseroles, purées and as a side dish with meat or poultry.
Storage: Store wrapped, unwashed in the refrigerator for a few days.
Nutritional Analysis: 5 sprouts (3.5 oz.) have 40 calories, 15% RDA Vitamin A, 108% RDA Vitamin C, are a good source of Vitamins B1, B6, Folacin,

Vitamins E, K, and Potassium, and less than one gram of fat, and are a good source of dietary fiber.

Cabbage
Availability: Year round. Another nutritious crucifer which varies from green to crinkly green (called Savoy) to red.
What to look for: Choose heavy, compact, fresh-looking heads. Avoid wilt or discoloration.
Uses: Use cabbage raw in cole slaw and salads combined with carrots, apples, oranges, onions, nuts and raisins. Cook cabbage to make sauerkraut, boil it to accompany corned beef, braise it, stuff it, stir-fry it, steam it, or add it to soups.
Storage: Store cabbage loosely wrapped in the refrigerator for a week or so.
Nutritional Analysis: ⅙ head (6 oz.) has 30 calories, 140% RDA Vitamin C, is a good source of Vitamins E and K, Folacin, and Potassium, and has less than one gram of fat and is a good source of dietary fiber.

Chinese Cabbage (Bok Choy)
Availability: Year round. This quick-cooking vegetable

**Guide to
Selecting
Produce**

Nutritional Rating:

Excellent Source is
if a food contains
20% or more of the
Recommended
Daily Intake
(RDI).

Good Source is
if a food contains
between 10 and
19% of the RDI.

with long green leaves and
slender stalks is also member of
the cruciferous family. Bok Choy
is an excellent source of calcium.
What to look for: Choose plump,
unblemished stalks with fresh green
leaves. Avoid rust and wilt.
Uses: Blanch, steam, braise, or
stir-fry, use in soups, salads,
dumplings and vegetable dishes.
Season with soy sauce, ginger,
garlic, rice wine, chilis and
sesame oil.
Storage: Store wrapped in damp
paper in the refrigerator for a
few days.
Nutritional Analysis: One cup
cooked (6 oz) has 20 calories
and is a good source of
Potassium and Vitamin A.

Cantaloupe
Availability: May to October.
This member of the melon
family is sweet, satisfying, very
low in calories and an excellent
source of Vitamins A and C.
What to look for: Cantaloupes
fall from the vine when they are
ripe, leaving a smooth scar on
the stem end. Look for this
feature as well as a fragrant aroma,
slightly golden under-color and
heavily netted skin. Pick heavy
melons with a slightly soft stem

end. Tap them and they should
sound hollow.
Uses: Serve cantaloupes at
breakfast or as a dessert or
appetizer sprinkled with lemon
or lime juice. Add to fruit salads,
combine with cold crab or shrimp
or purée to use as a cold soup or
topping.
Storage: Store at room temperature
until fully ripe, then refrigerate
well-wrapped if cut for a few days.
Nutritional Analysis: ½ small
cantaloupe (6 oz.) has 50
calories, 100% RDA Vitamin A,
110% RDA Vitamin C, is a good
source of Folacin and Potassium,
has less than one gram of fat and
is a good source of dietary fiber.

Carrots
Availability: Year round.
Carrots are versatile, delicious
and nutritious. They are
inexpensive, easy-to-store, and
add color and flavor to a wide
variety of dishes.
What to look for: Select firm,
plump, crisp, bright orange carrots
that are smooth and shiny with
fresh-looking greens attached, if
any. Avoid greenish coloring, wilt,
shrivel, rot, cracks or hairy roots.
Uses: Carrots are delicious raw
as a snack or in salads and

Guide to Selecting Produce

Nutritional Rating:

Excellent Source is if a food contains 20% or more of the Recommended Daily Intake (RDI).

Good Source is if a food contains between 10 and 19% of the RDI.

crudité. Steam, simmer, boil, bake, stir-fry, stew or purée. Add to soups and stews. Shred carrots to add to cakes and muffins.
Storage: Store carrots wrapped in the refrigerator for up to two weeks. Be sure to remove the tops for storage as they continue to draw moisture and wilt the carrots.
Nutritional Analysis: One medium carrot (2.8 oz.) has 40 calories, 330% RDA Vitamin A, less than one gram of fat and is a good source of dietary fiber.

Cauliflower
Availability: Year round. Another nutritious member of the cabbage family that is delicious raw or cooked. Cauliflower appears in white, purple and green varieties.
What to look for: Choose ivory-colored, heavy, solid, tight unblemished heads with fresh green leaves.
Uses: Use cauliflower raw in crudité and salads. Steam, boil, blanch or stir-fry this vegetable which works well with a variety of sauces. It may also be puréed, curried, pickled or deep-fried. Cauliflower stem and greens work well in soups and stir-fries.
Storage: Store in the

refrigerator, wrapped loosely for a few days.
Nutritional Analysis: ¼ of a small head (5.3 oz.) has 25 calories, 160% RDA Vitamin C, less than one gram of fat, and is a good source of dietary fiber.

Celery
Availability: Year round. Crisp and crunchy, celery is tasty both raw and cooked.
What to look for: Choose crisp, fresh, clean stalks that are plump, firm and heavy. Any leaves should be perky and bright green.
Uses: Raw, it is eaten plain or with dips, added to salads and cole slaws and often stuffed with tuna fish, cheese or peanut butter. Cooked celery is used in stir-fries, stews, soups and stuffings or braised on its own.
Storage: Store wrapped celery in the refrigerator for a few days.
Nutritional Analysis: 2 large stalks (4.25 oz.) have 20 calories, 15% RDA Vitamin C, less than one gram of fat, and are a good source of dietary fiber.

Cherries
Availability: May to August. Cherries are a sweet, juicy and delicious summer treat.

Guide to Selecting Produce

Nutritional Rating:

Excellent Source is if a food contains 20% or more of the Recommended Daily Intake (RDI).

Good Source is if a food contains between 10 and 19% of the RDI.

What to look for: Look for deep, dark red cherries that are glossy, firm and plump with stems still attached.

Uses: Eat fresh or add to fruit salads. Use in cakes, pies, tarts, preserves, jams and jellies or in a sauce for duck.

Storage: Store loosely wrapped in the refrigerator for up to two days.

Nutritional Analysis: ½ cup has 49 calories, is a good source of Vitamin C and Potassium, less than one gram of fat.

Corn

Availability: Year round. Prime season is June to October. Corn is best eaten soon after harvesting as its sugar turns to starch with time.

What to look for: Choose green, moist pliant husks with fresh-looking silk and cobs that are covered with plump, even rows of kernels.

Uses: Corn is delicious combined with tomatoes, beans, squash, peppers, greens, sweet potatoes, pasta and any meat and poultry.

Storage: Store in husk in the refrigerator for one or two days.

Nutritional Analysis: ½ cup has 89 calories, one gram of fat.

Cucumbers

Availability: Year round. Cucumbers range in size from little gherkins to giant seedless varieties. Two common types are the large, dark-green cucumbers and the smaller, sweeter Kirbies.

What to look for: Choose firm, plump, green cucumbers that are small for their type. Avoid white or yellowish areas as well as shriveling or soft, watery spots.

Uses: Use cucumbers in salads seasoned with yogurt, vinegar, dill, parsley and mustard. Use in chutneys, pickle, steam or sauté. Stuff cucumbers or add them to sandwiches.

Storage: Store cucumbers wrapped in the refrigerator for a few days.

Nutritional Analysis: ½ cup has 7 calories, less than one gram of fat.

Eggplant

Availability: Year round. A meaty, satisfying vegetable which comes in a variety of sizes, colors, and forms, the most common of which is purple and pear-shaped.

What to look for: Choose plump, firm, glossy, eggplants that feel heavy for their size and bounce back gently when pressed. Avoid very large eggplants which tend to be spongy and full of seeds.
Uses: Eggplants can be broiled, steamed, baked, stuffed, roasted, sautéed, puréed, fried or stir-fried. Delicious combined with tomatoes, onions, garlic, peppers, squash, meat and poultry, cheese, seafood, herbs, breading, olive oil, lemon juice and tahini or sesame oil.
Storage: Store wrapped in the refrigerator for a few days.
Nutritional Analysis: ½ cup has 13 calories, less than one gram of fat.

Grapefruit
Availability: Year round. Prime season is December to April. A refreshing citrus fruit, grapefruit is at its best in midwinter.
What to look for: Choose firm, smooth-textured, plump, round, heavy fruit that is either bright yellow or yellowish pink. Avoid bruised or lightweight grapefruits.
Uses: Eat grapefruit at any meal or as a snack or appetizer.

Squeeze it for juice, add it to fruit salads, mix it with greens and avocado, broil with a little brown sugar or use it to make ices and sherbet.
Storage: Store grapefruit in the refrigerator for up to a week.
Nutritional Analysis: ½ grapefruit (4.2 oz) has 38 calories, 69% RDA Vitamin C, less than one gram of fat.

Grapes
Availability: Year round. Prime season is late summer and early fall. Grapes are harvested only once a year and fruit picked too early will not ripen. Grapes come as green or purple varieties, with or without seeds.
What to look for: Choose plump, firm grapes with a slightly frosty film on the skin called a bloom. Look for grapes that have fresh greenish stems.
Uses: Eat fresh washed grapes or add to fruit salads, tarts, chicken salads, and seafood and poultry sauces. Grapes also make delicious jams, jellies and preserves.
Storage: Store grapes unwashed and loosely wrapped in the refrigerator for a few days.
Nutritional Analysis: One cup

has 58 calories, good source of
Vitamins B1, C, E, and Potassium,
less than one gram of fat

Green Beans
Availability: Year round. Peak
season is April to September.
What to look for: Select small,
slender, bright green beans that
break in two with a snapping
sound. Avoid shriveled ends, wilt,
blemishes and overgrown beans.
Uses: Eat raw or cooked. Green
beans are delicious steamed,
sautéed, stir-fried or simmered.
Use as a side dish with meats or
add to salads, soups, stews,
casseroles and stir-fries.
Storage: Store in a bag in the
refrigerator for a few days.
Nutritional Analysis: ½ cup has
22 calories, less than one gram
of fat.

Kale
Availability: Year round. Prime
season is October to April.
Kale is a highly nutritious
member of the cabbage family, a
fine source of Calcium, Beta
Carotene, Vitamin A, and Iron.
What to look for: Choose
fresh, crisp, bright green leaves.
Avoid yellowing leaves and
coarse stems as well as rot and

insect damage.
Uses: Young, tender leaves may
be used in salads. Cook larger,
older leaves and use them in
soups, stews, stir-fries, or alone
seasoned with garlic, onions,
olive oil, or vinegar. Delicious
combined with rice, beans, corn,
potatoes, meat and poultry.
Storage: Store in the
refrigerator unwashed and
wrapped for a few days.
Nutritional Analysis: One cup
raw kale (2.4 oz.) has 33
calories, 120% RDA Vitamin A,
134% RDA Vitamin C, is a good
source of Vitamins B1 and B2,
Calcium, Iron, Magnesium, and
Potassium, less than one gram of
fat, and is a good source of
dietary fiber.

Kiwi Fruit
Availability: Year round.
Kiwis are egg-shaped, brown
fuzzy fruits whose bright green
pulps have a wonderful sweet-
tart balance and are highly
nutritious. Originally from New
Zealand, the kiwi is now available
all over the United States. They
are also known as Chinese
gooseberries.
What to look for: Pick fruit
that is slightly soft to the touch

Guide to Selecting Produce

Nutritional Rating:

Excellent Source is if a food contains 20% or more of the Recommended Daily Intake (RDI).

Good Source is if a food contains between 10 and 19% of the RDI.

and ripen for a few days at room temperature until soft and sweet-smelling but not mushy. Avoid kiwis that are rock-hard or soft, bruised and shriveled.
Uses: Peel kiwis and add them to fruit salads, tarts, cakes, pies and poultry salads. Serve with thinly sliced prosciutto as an appetizer.
Storage: Store ripe kiwis in the refrigerator for a few days.
Nutritional Analysis: Two kiwis (5.3 oz.) have 90 calories, 230% RDA Vitamin C, less than one gram of fat and are a good source of dietary fiber.

Kohlrabi
Availability: Year round.
A member of the cabbage family, one can eat both the bulb and the tops of kohlrabi.
What to look for: Choose smaller plants with bright green, fresh-looking leaves.
Uses: The tops can be stir-fried, steamed, sautéed and added to soups and stews. The bulbs can be used raw in salads or with dips or boiled, steamed or stir-fried.
Storage: Store in the refrigerator for up to a week.
Nutritional Analysis: One cup sliced (8 oz) has 38 calories,

145% RDA Vitamin C, good source of Vitamin B6 and Potassium, less than one gram of fat, and is a good source of fiber.

Leeks
Availability: Year round. Prime season is October to April.
A sweet member of the onion family.
What to look for: Choose smaller leeks with fresh, long, straight white stems and roots at least partially intact and green leaves.
Uses: Use the greens to flavor stocks, soups and stews and the white stems in stir-fries and other quick-cooking dishes. Braise and serve as a side dish. Add to meat, fish, other vegetables, pastas and stir-fries.
Storage: Store unwashed in the refrigerator for a few days.
Nutritional Analysis: ½ cup has 16 calories, one gram of fat.

Lemons and Limes
Availability: Year round.
Lemons are used universally in a wide variety of cuisines. Limes also serve many uses.
What to look for: Look for thin-skinned fruit that is plump, firm and heavy for its size. Avoid fruit that is moldy or lightweight,

soft or shriveled.
Uses: Use both the juice and
zest (the thin, outer colored layer
of the peel) for flavoring. Use
lemon juice for seafood, meat,
poultry, fruits, vegetables, drinks
and baked goods. Limes are more
often used in Central American,
Caribbean, Indian, Southeast
Asian and Polynesian cookery.
Sliced, they make attractive
garnishes for drinks, cold dishes
and salads.
Storage: Store in the refrigerator
for up to two weeks.
Nutritional Analysis: One
medium lemon or lime has 20
calories, is a good source of
Vitamin C, and has less than one
gram of fat.

Head Lettuce
Availability: Year round. Prime
seasons are spring and fall.
The most common varieties are
Bibb iceberg, and Boston.
What to look for: Choose fresh,
crisp heads and avoid wilt,
browning and rot.
Uses: Use in salads, sandwiches,
and stir-fries. Steam, braise and
add to soups. Dress salads just
before serving.
Storage: Store wrapped in the
refrigerator for a few days.

Nutritional Analysis: ¼ head
iceberg (4.75 oz) has 25 calories,
no fat and is a good source of
dietary fiber.

Leaf Lettuce and Romaine
Availability: Year round. Prime
seasons are spring and fall.
The most common varieties are
red leaf, green leaf and romaine.
What to look for: Select crisp,
green leaves. Avoid rot, rust and
wilt. Darker leafed types are the
most nutritious.
Uses: Use in salads and
sandwiches. Steam, braise and
add to soups.
Storage: Wrap and store in the
refrigerator for a few days.
Nutritional Analysis: ½ cup has
5 calories, good source of
Vitamins A, B1, C, K, Folacin,
Manganese, and Potassium, no
fat and is a good source of
dietary fiber.

Mangoes
Availability: Year round. Prime
season is May through September.
The sweet, fragrant orange-
fleshed mango is best when tree-
ripened or nearly so.
What to look for: Choose
plump heavy fruit with a smooth
skin that has at least begun to

turn yellow-orange, which yields slightly to pressure and has a fresh scent. Very green or rock-hard mangoes will never ripen.

Uses: Eat mangoes alone or use in fruit salads, chutneys, relishes, ice creams and ices and baked goods. Season with lime juice. Add to duck sauces.

Storage: Store ripened fruit in the refrigerator for a day or two.

Nutritional Analysis: One medium has 135 calories, good source of Vitamins A, B6, C, E, and Potassium, and less than one gram of fat.

Cultivated Mushrooms

Availability: Year round. Cultivated mushrooms vary from very smooth and white to off-white and tan and sometimes even scaly. Size varies as well but does not affect quality.

What to look for: Look for fresh, plump, round, firm mushrooms with tightly rounded caps that are closed around the stem. Mushrooms should be fairly clean, have little or no aroma and the skin should not be slimy.

Uses: Eat mushrooms raw in salads and crudités or stuff, bake, broil, fry, sauté, stew, marinate or pickle mushrooms

to use in a variety of dishes. Add them to stir-fries, soups and sauces. Mushrooms absorb a great deal of liquid or fat and should never be soaked. The best way to clean mushrooms is to use a damp cloth or soft brush.

Storage: Store in a paper bag in the refrigerator for up to a week.

Nutritional Analysis: ½ cup has 9 calories, less than one gram of fat.

Wild Mushrooms

Availability: Year round. Prime season is September through January. Examples of wild mushrooms are Chanterelles which have a curving, yellow-to-orange trumpet-shaped cap. They have a chewy texture and are often stewed. Enoki, small Japanese mushrooms that are tender and have a mild flavor. They work well in salads, soups, and stir-fried dishes. Morels, rare and expensive, have wrinkled, elongated caps and a rich earthy flavor. Often found dried, Morels work well in stuffings and cream sauces. Oyster mushrooms are named for their soft gray color and shape. They have a firm, meaty texture and go well with meat and fish dishes. Shitake mushrooms have dark caps, a meaty consistency,

Guide to Selecting Produce

Nutritional Rating:

Excellent Source is if a food contains 20% or more of the Recommended Daily Intake (RDI).

Good Source is if a food contains between 10 and 19% of the RDI.

and a strong woody taste. Shitakes are delicious in soups, stir-fries, sauces, stews and casseroles.
Nutritional Analysis: Four Shitake have 40 calories, less than one gram of fat. One large Enoki has two calories and no fat.

Okra
Availability: Year round. Prime season is summer. Okra contains mucilaginous materials that give it a characteristic sticky or slimy texture when cooked.
What to look for: Choose fresh, young, tender, bright-green small-to-medium-sized pods.
Uses: Okra may be steamed or combined with other ingredients such as onions, peppers, corn, and tomatoes. Okra is the famous ingredient of Louisiana stews called gumbo. Okra may also be fried in cornmeal. It's delicious in a variety of other vegetable and meat dishes as well.
Storage: Store wrapped in the refrigerator for a few days.
Nutritional Analysis: ½ cup has 25 calories, less than one gram of fat.

Onions
Availability: Year round. Onions come in a variety of shapes and sizes: round, spherical, flattened, or spindle-shaped and they may be white, yellow, or red.
What to look for: Choose onions that are firm and heavy for their size with dry, papery skins. Avoid onions that have begun to sprout or soften.
Uses: Use onions either raw or cooked in a variety of dishes such as soups, salads, stews, stir-fries, sauces and sandwiches. The longer an onion is cooked, the milder its flavor and aroma.
Storage: Store onions in a dark, cool, dry, well-ventilated place for up to two months.
Nutritional Analysis: One medium onion (5.3 oz.) has 65 calories, 15% RDA Vitamin C, good source of Folacin, less than one gram of fat and is a good source of dietary fiber.

Oranges
Availability: Year round. Prime season is December through May. Oranges make up the leading citrus crop in the United States. Two of the most common sweet oranges are Valencia oranges

Guide to Selecting Produce

Nutritional Rating:

Excellent Source is if a food contains 20% or more of the Recommended Daily Intake (RDI).

Good Source is if a food contains between 10 and 19% of the RDI.

with thin skin and high juice content which make them best for juicing, and Navel oranges with thick peel which is fairly easy to remove and sweet taste which make them delicious eating oranges.

What to look for: Choose heavy, plump, firm oranges. Color does not indicate quality, but rather is the result of the variety and climate.

Uses: Use oranges to make juice or eat them raw, in fruit and green salads, or use them to flavor seafood, poultry and desserts. Sliced, they make excellent garnishes.

Storage: Store oranges wrapped in the refrigerator for up to two weeks.

Nutritional Analysis: One orange (4.6 oz.) has 62 calories, 116% RDA Vitamin C, is a good source of Vitamin B1, Folacin, and Potassium and has less than one gram of fat.

Papayas

Availability: Late March to Late June.

This delicious orange fruit that turns yellow when ripe has a sweet, melon-like flavor.

What to look for: Look for firm papayas that have already begun to turn yellow.

Uses: Papayas are delicious eaten alone, stuffed with seafood or poultry salad or ice cream or added to fruit and green salads. They may also be puréed for use as ices, ice cream or beverages.

Storage: Ripen papayas at room temperature until golden and soft, then refrigerate for up to a week.

Nutritional Analysis: ½ papaya (5.3 oz.) has 80 calories, 160% RDA Vitamin C, good source of Vitamin A, Folacin, and Potassium, less than one gram of fat, and is a good source of dietary fiber. They contain papain, a protein digesting enzyme.

Peaches and Nectarines

Availability: May to October. Ancient fruits from China, these two summer treats are nearly interchangeable.

What to look for: Choose peaches and nectarines that have no trace of green color and have a fragrant aroma. Look for fruit that is firm but not rock-hard.

Uses: Peaches and nectarines are delicious eaten alone or in fruit salads, green salads, pies, tarts, cakes, cobblers, ice cream,

preserves, relishes and meat dishes.
Storage: Ripen at room temperature, then refrigerate for up to a week.
Nutritional Analysis: One medium peach or nectarine has 67 calories, is a good source of Vitamin C and Potassium and has less than one gram of fat.

Pears
Availability: August to March. There are a large variety of pears on the market such as the roundish, sweet, juicy Comice, miniature, sweet Seckels, the long-necked Bosc and the pale green or reddish Anjou. You may be able to find pears year round but you will have a hard time finding one worth eating in the spring and early summer. Pears ripen from the inside out.
What to look for: Select large, firm, unblemished pears.
Uses: Pears are delicious eaten fresh, baked, poached, stewed, in salads, tarts, and other desserts. They go well with vegetables, nuts and dairy products such as cheese and ice cream.
Storage: Ripen pears at room temperature until they reach the desired softness, then eat or refrigerate for a few days.

Nutritional Analysis: One medium pear has 98 calories, less than one gram of fat.

Peas: Snow-Peas, Green Peas, Petits Pois, Mange Tout and Sugar Snap Peas
Availability: Snow peas - Year round. Green peas, petits pois, mange tout and sugar snap peas - February to July.
Like sweet corn, the sugar in peas turns to starch immediately after picking, which is why so many people use the frozen kind. Green or English peas are the most popular. Only the seed inside the pod is edible. Snow peas are also quite common. They have flat, edible pods and tiny seeds. Sugar snap peas, a combination of the first two, have tender, crisp edible pods and sweet little seeds too.
What to look for: Choose peas with crisp, small, vibrantly green, glossy pods and fresh ends.
Uses: Peas are delicious briefly steamed or simmered, eaten alone or added to salads, soups, purées, stews and stir-fries.
Storage: Store peas in the refrigerator for a day or two.
Nutritional Analysis: ½ cup green peas has 58 calories, less

Guide to Selecting Produce

Nutritional Rating:

Excellent Source is if a food contains 20% or more of the Recommended Daily Intake (RDI).

Good Source is if a food contains between 10 and 19% of the RDI.

than one gram of fat, ½ cup snow peas has 35 calories and no fat.

Bell Peppers
Availability: Year round.
The pepper was inaccurately named by Columbus who reasoned that these fruits of the vine must be related to peppercorns because of their hot flavor. Peppers come in a variety of colors: green, yellow, orange, red, purple, and white. Some, like the red, which are green peppers that have been left on the vine to ripen further, are particularly sweet. The green ones tend to be more peppery and less expensive.
What to look for: Pick peppers that are firm and heavy for their size with tight, glossy skin. Avoid peppers with blemishes or soft spots.
Uses: Peppers are extremely versatile. They can be eaten raw in salads and crudités as well as cooked in vegetable, meat and seafood dishes. They can be steamed, roasted, stewed, sautéed, fried, stir-fried, baked, stuffed and pickled.
Storage: Store peppers in the refrigerator for a few days.
Nutritional Analysis: One pepper (5.25 oz.) has 25 calories, 130% RDA Vitamin C,

good source of Vitamins A, B6, E, Folacin, and Potassium, less than one gram of fat, and is a good source of dietary fiber.

Pineapple
Availability: Year round. Hawaii has the largest pineapple industry in the world, although these fruits are grown in other tropical areas as well. Hawaiian pineapples are usually the sweetest and largest. Pineapples cannot be ripened once they are picked so be sure to choose a ripe one.
What to look for: Choose pineapples with some yellow and very little green coloring, a sweet, fresh fragrance, green, fresh-looking crowns and tender but not overly soft bottoms.
Uses: Pineapples are delicious in salads, main courses, particularly pork dishes, desserts, beverages and preserves.
Storage: Store pineapples either in the refrigerator or at room temperature for a few days.
Nutritional Analysis: One cup has 77 calories, is a good source of Vitamins B1 and C, and Manganese, and less than one gram of fat. Pineapples contain the enzyme bromelain which helps digest protein (see papain in papaya also).

Plums

Availability: May to October.
A cousin of peaches and nectarines, plums come in a variety of colors, shapes, and sizes.

What to look for: Choose plump, soft, tight-skinned plums with a deep, even color.

Uses: Eat plums fresh, or add them to fruit salads, pies, tarts, cakes, ices and ice creams. They are delicious poached or stewed. Use them in preserves and jellies and meat dishes, especially duck, goose, and pork.

Storage: Ripen fruit at room temperature if necessary, then store in the refrigerator for up to five days.

Nutritional Analysis: One medium plum has 36 calories, less than one gram of fat.

Potatoes

Availability: Year round.
Potatoes are an extremely versatile vegetable and a good source of potassium and vitamin C (if unpeeled). Potatoes generally fall into two categories: waxy and starchy. The waxy potatoes, such as red new potatoes, also known as Red Bliss, have a moist, waxy quality and are best boiled or steamed. Starchy potatoes, such as Idaho Russets are dryer and are best baked, fried, or mashed.

What to look for: Select potatoes that are firm, plump, and smooth with no soft dark areas, cuts, or sprouts. Sprouting potatoes may still be used as long as the potato is still firm and the sprouts are removed.

Storage: Store potatoes in a cool, dry, dark, well-ventilated place for up to a month. Do not refrigerate as this causes the starch in the potatoes to turn to sugar.

Nutritional Analysis: One medium potato (5.3 oz.) has 110 calories, 50% RDA Vitamin C, is a good source of Vitamins B1, B6, Niacin, Pantothenic acid, K, Copper, Magnesium, and Potassium, less than one gram of fat, and is a good source of dietary fiber.

Spinach

Availability: Year round.
Spinach is a good source of iron as well as potassium and Vitamin A. Spinach is grown in sandy soil and so must be washed carefully soaking briefly in water a few times is the best method.

What to look for: Look for spinach with smaller, dark green, crisp, fresh-looking leaves.

Uses: Spinach is delicious eaten raw in a salad or briefly steamed in its own moisture.

Storage: Store spinach in a bag in the refrigerator for a few days.

Nutritional Analysis: One cup raw spinach (2 oz.) has 12 calories, 68% RDA Vitamin A, 26% RDA Vitamin C, is an excellent source of Folacin and Iron and is a good source of dietary fiber. It contains less than one gram of fat.

Summer Squash

Availability: Year round. Prime season is March to October. Summer squashes are immature fruits with soft skins and edible seeds which, if left on the plant, will mature into hard-skinned, large winter squashes. The most common types of summer squash are zucchini and yellow squash which come straight or crook-necked.

What to look for: Choose small, firm, unblemished squashes that are heavy for their size.

Uses: Zucchini and yellow squash may be eaten raw in salads and crudités or lightly steamed or sautéed. They are delicious with other vegetables such as onions,

tomatoes, garlic, eggplant, and peppers. They may also be fried, stuffed and baked or stir-fried.

Storage: Store squash wrapped in the refrigerator for up to four days.

Nutritional Analysis: One cup has 29 calories, is a good source of Folacin, Vitamin C, Magnesium, and Potassium, and has less than one gram of fat.

Winter Squash

Availability: August to March. Winter squash are planted in the summer and harvested in the summer or fall. They are called winter squashes because they may be stored for long periods of time. There are a variety of types of winter squash, most of which have slightly sweet, nutty tasting orange flesh which must be cooked. Some examples are Acorn, Hubbard, Butternut, Kabocha, Buttercup, Delicata and Pumpkin. All are good sources of Vitamin A and fiber.

What to look for: Choose heavy squashes with smooth, hard, unblemished rinds.

Uses: Bake, steam or simmer squash. They are delicious stuffed or used to make purées, soups, stews, puddings and pies.

Storage: Store squash in a cool,

Guide to Selecting Produce

Nutritional Rating:

Excellent Source is if a food contains 20% or more of the Recommended Daily Intake (RDI).

Good Source is if a food contains between 10 and 19% of the RDI.

dry, dark, well-ventilated place for up to two months.
Nutritional Analysis: One cup (4 oz.) has 43 calories, 94% RDA Vitamin A, 23% RDA Vitamin C, a good source of Folacin and Potassium, less than one gram of fat, and is a good source of dietary fiber.

Strawberries
Availability: February to September.
What to look for: Choose plump, firm, dry, unblemished berries that are fully colored and have the cap stem still attached. Avoid cartons with seepage of juice on the bottom which may indicate that the berries inside are soft.
Uses: Strawberries are delicious eaten raw on cereal or in salads combined with other fruit, poultry, nuts, nut oils and greens. Use them to make pies, tarts, cakes, muffins, cobblers, preserves, jellies, syrups, ice creams and ices.
Storage: Store berries wrapped in the refrigerator and do not remove stems or wash berries until you are ready to use them.
Nutritional Analysis: One cup (5.3 oz.) has 45 calories, 140% RDA Vitamin C, is a good

source of Folacin, Vitamin K, Manganese and Potassium, less than one gram of fat and is a good source of dietary fiber.

Sweet Potatoes
Availability: Year round. Prime season is September to January. There is much confusion between sweet potatoes and yams. Both are tubers that are similar in appearance and flavor but they are from completely different plants. What some stores sell as yams are actually dark, orange-fleshed sweet potatoes. These are more moist, sweet, and more flavorful than the paler-yellow ones.
What to look for: Choose firm, small-to medium-sized potatoes that taper towards the ends and have bright, smooth, unblemished skin.
Uses: Sweet potatoes have dozens of uses. They may be baked and eaten as is, or fried, candied, puréed, mashed or used in casseroles, soufflés, stews, soups, bread, muffins, pie, cakes and cookies.
Storage: Store sweet potatoes in a dry, cool, dark, well-ventilated place for up to ten days.
Nutritional Analysis: One

Guide to Selecting Produce

Nutritional Rating:

Excellent Source is if a food contains 20% or more of the Recommended Daily Intake (RDI).

Good Source is if a food contains between 10 and 19% of the RDI.

medium sweet potato (4.5 oz.) has 136 calories, 522% RDA Vitamin A, 50% RDA Vitamin C, less than one gram of fat and is a good source of dietary fiber.

Tomatoes
Availability: Year round. Prime season is June to October. Vine ripe or cherry tomatoes are the most flavorful.

What to look for: Choose fruit that are fragrant, red and plump and yield to gentle pressure. Vine ripe or cherry are most flavorful.

Uses: Use tomatoes in salads and sandwiches, soups, stews, and sauces for all variety of dishes from pasta and vegetables to meats, fish, and poultry. Tomatoes may be broiled, baked, fried, sautéed or stuffed. Plum tomatoes are the best for making sauces, and they are also good eaten fresh.

Storage: Ripen tomatoes at room temperature if necessary, then store in the refrigerator for a few days. However, refrigeration diminishes flavor.

Nutritional Analysis: One medium (5.3 oz.) has 35 calories, 40% RDA Vitamin C, 20% RDA Vitamin A, a good source of Potassium, less than one gram of fat and is a good source of dietary fiber.

Watermelon
Availability: May to October. The best watermelons are ready at the height of summer, a time when their sweet, refreshing juiciness is very welcome. Plus they are low in calories and high in vitamins A and C.

What to look for: Choose watermelons that are firm, and heavy with fresh-looking outer skin and which sound hollow when tapped. A watermelon's flesh should be deeply colored with mature black seeds if the seeded variety. Lots of white seeds indicate the melon was picked too early.

Uses: Watermelons are delicious alone or in fruit salads. Use them as bowls from which to serve fruit salads and beverages.

Storage: Store watermelon in the refrigerator for a few days. Whole watermelon will keep longer than cut.

Nutritional Analysis: One cup has 50 calories, is a good source of Vitamins B6 and C and has less than one gram of fat.

CULINARY HERBS

Herbs are the leaves and stems of plants used to add their characteristic flavors to cooking. **Uses:** Use fresh herbs rather than dried whenever possible. Use three to five times more fresh herbs than dried. For fullest flavor, add at least half of the fresh herbs at the end of cooking. **Storage:** Snip the bottoms of the stems and set the unwashed herbs in a glass of water. Cover with a plastic bag secured to the glass with a rubber band or string. Store in the refrigerator for five to seven days, changing the water regularly; however, the herbs will begin to lose flavor after the third day.

Basil

Availability: Year round. Prime season is April to September. Basil is a member of the mint family and can be found with either green or purple leaves. Basil is intensely aromatic and has a licorice-like flavor. **What to look for:** Select fresh, brightly colored leaves. Avoid yellowing, rust, wilt and flower buds. **Uses:** Use with tomatoes, either raw or cooked, in pesto sauces, soups, stews, casseroles, salads, pastas, pizzas, egg dishes and curries. Use to flavor oils and vinegars. Add basil to onions, eggplant, zucchini and peppers. Combine with garlic and olive oil to add flavor to meat and fish.

Bay Leaves

Availability: Year round. **Uses:** Fresh or dried, use as part of herb bouquets to flavor stews, soups, stocks, stuffings, marinades and sauces. Bay leaves also enhance pot roast and roast chicken. Use sparingly and be sure to remove the bay leaves before serving as they are not meant to be eaten. **Storage:** Store fresh leaves in the refrigerator wrapped in damp paper.

Borage

Availability: Year round. **Uses:** Young leaves make a refreshing addition to salads. Older leaves can be used for seasoning in cooked dishes. Borage's blue flowers can be eaten raw or crystallized.

Catnip

Availability: Year round. **Uses:** A favorite of cats as well as humans who use the leaves or flowers to make tea.

Chamomile
Availability: Year round.
A daisy-like plant noted for its medicinal, healing and calming qualities. Good source of Vitamin A.
Uses: Chamomile flowers are used as a sedative tea. Its leaves also have a calming effect.

Chervil
Availability: Year round.
Chervil is an aromatic herb with lacy, fern-like leaves. Its flavor is reminiscent of tarragon.
Uses: Chervil complements green salads and potato salads, as well as egg, tomato and fish dishes. Add it to cream soups, mayonnaise and herb butters and sauces.

Chives
Availability: Year round.
Chives are a slender, green, hollow-stemmed member of the onion family.
Uses: Always use fresh chives raw as their flavor is mild and gets lost in cooking. Chives are good additions to bean and grain salads as well as eggs, potatoes, fish and creamy soups. They also add great flavor to sour cream and cream cheese.

Cilantro (Chinese Parsley, Coriander)
Availability: Year round.
This small-leafed, green herb looks a bit like flat-leafed Italian parsley but its leaves are broader and shorter. It is distinguished by its pungent flavor and aroma.
Uses: Cilantro is commonly used in Asian, Latin American and Spanish dishes, especially with shrimp, fish, tomatoes and in soups, stews and salsas.

Dill
Availability: Year round.
This herb with its delicate, feathery leaves is used in a variety of cuisines, most notably Scandinavian and Eastern European. Dill is a member of the parsley family.
Uses: Use dill fresh or add it at the end of cooking as heat diminishes its flavor. Add it to vegetables and seafood. It is delicious in salads, especially cucumber salads, cream sauces, savory breads and soups. Dill seeds are pressed for an oil used to flavor pickles.

Garlic
Availability: Year round.
A member of the onion family touted for its medicinal qualities.

Garlic is rich in sulfurous compounds with proven antibacterial powers.

Uses: Depending on how it is used, garlic's flavor ranges from pungent and hot to sweet and mild. Whole, unpeeled garlic is the most mild. Garlic mashed to a paste is much stronger. Garlic simmered in liquid will be mild, sautéed in hot fat will be more pungent. Garlic enhances innumerable foods such as soups, salads, sauces, breads, meats, fish, vegetables and eggs.

What to look for: Choose bulbs that feel full, firm and heavy. Avoid bulbs with sprouting, rot, mildew or soft darkened cloves.

Storage: Store garlic in a cool, dry, well-ventilated place for a month or so. Try to leave heads whole as individual cloves dry out rapidly.

Nutritional Analysis: Garlic is a good source of Vitamins B1 and C, Potassium, Calcium, Copper, Iron, Magnesium, Phosphorus, Potassium and Selenium.

Ginger

Availability: Year round. Fresh ginger root is both sweet and hot at the same time and is versatile in the kitchen.

What to look for: Choose ginger with a smooth skin and a slight gloss and plump, firm roots with few knobs and small branchings that have an aromatic scent. Ginger also comes in powdered, crystallized, preserved and pickled forms.

Uses: Fresh ginger root is used in Asian, Middle Eastern and Mediterranean cooking. It can be used to flavor both sweet and savory foods from gingerbread to stir-fries.

Storage: Store ginger loosely wrapped in the refrigerator for two to three weeks or in the freezer.

Nutritional Analysis: Ginger is a good source of Vitamins B6 and C, Magnesium and Potassium.

Horseradish

Availability: Fresh horseradish root is available fall through spring. This member of the cabbage family is a pungent root with a thin, rough, brown skin and white flesh.

What to look for: Choose roots that are fresh-looking with no blemishes. Horseradish also comes bottled alone or mixed with beetroot.

Uses: Horseradish is rarely

cooked. It is generally used raw as a condiment or is added to other condiments. Grated horseradish is a common ingredient in cocktail sauces for shellfish. Mixed with sour cream or whipped cream, it complements meats and fish. It also enhances cream dressings for cole slaw and beets.
Storage: Store fresh horseradish in a paper bag inside a plastic bag in the refrigerator for up to a week.

Lemongrass
Availability: Year round.
Also known as citronella, this tropical grass has yellow-white stems, gray-green blades and a lemony aroma.
What to look for: Pick firm, unblemished stalks.
Uses: Lemongrass is an essential ingredient in Southeast Asian cooking. It is used to make soups, sautés and fish dishes as well as curry pastes and stir-fries.
Storage: Store in the refrigerator crisper for up to two months.

Lovage
Availability: Year round.
A large plant that looks and tastes like celery.
Uses: Lovage is used in salads, stews, stuffings, vegetable dishes and soups.

Marjoram
Availability: Year round.
This member of the mint family is extremely similar to oregano both botanically and with regard to flavor, although marjoram is a bit more sweet and mild.
Uses: Because of its delicate flavor, marjoram is best used when added at the end of cooking. Marjoram works well with veal, pork, lamb and poultry, salads, vegetables, pasta sauces and eggs. Add it to meat loaves, sausage mixtures, soups and stuffings.

Mint
Availability: Year round.
There are several varieties of mint, each with a different pungency. Spearmint is most often used in cooking. Mints have a sweet, slightly hot flavor, a cool after taste and a pungent aroma.
Uses: Add to fruit salads, cole slaw, ice creams, relishes, lamb or poultry dishes, tomato sauces, squash, yogurt and cucumbers, vegetable dishes, grain salads and tea. Mint can also be used instead of basil to make pesto sauce. It is also used in chutneys and curries.

Oregano
Availability: Year round.
This pungent herb, a member of the mint family, is also known as wild marjoram.
Uses: Use oregano to flavor seafood, poultry, lamb, other grilled meats, pizza, bean soups, stews, tomatoes and other vegetables.

Parsley
Availability: Year round.
This versatile herb is used more than almost any other to season salads and cooked dishes. It is nutritious and low in calories and price. Parsley comes in two common varieties: curly and flat-leafed or Italian.
Uses: Use parsley as a garnish as well as in salads, soups, sauces, stews, and stocks. Combine with meat, poultry, seafood, eggs, cheeses, vegetables, beans, potatoes, grains, onions, garlic and shallots. Parsley is also used as a breath freshener.
Nutritional Analysis: Parsley is a good source of Vitamins A, C, and E, Niacin, Folacin, Calcium, Iron, Magnesium and Potassium.

Rosemary
Availability: Year round.
Rosemary is a highly aromatic herb with pointed, pine-shaped leaves.
Uses: Used to flavor breads, potatoes and other vegetables, beans, poultry, pork, lamb, veal, seafood as well as baked goods, jellies and sweets. Use sparingly. Rosemary is a good source of antioxidants.

Sage
Availability: Year round.
Uses: Sage is commonly used to flavor stuffings as well as meats and cheese. It is also good with grains and beans. Use sparingly.

Savory
Availability: Year round.
Savory comes in both summer and the more assertive winter varieties. The peppery flavor of both is reminiscent of thyme.
Uses: Both types of savory are used in sausages, stuffings, beans, fish and other soups, vegetable dishes, egg dishes, meat dishes and meat pies.

Tarragon
Availability: Year Round.
This delicate green herb has an anise-like flavor and aroma.
Uses: Use to season seafood, poultry, sauces, butters, eggs and salads as well as to flavor mayonnaise and vinegars.

Thyme

Availability: Year round.
This member of the mint family comes in a variety of forms and is almost as popular as parsley. It is commonly associated with French and Italian cookery.
Uses: Thyme is used in countless savory recipes. It is especially good with tomatoes, eggplant, onions and green beans, lamb, fish, veal and chicken. Add it to stews, soups, stuffings and bean dishes. Thyme is a good source of antioxidants.

CULINARY SPICES

Spices are usually dried, either whole or ground. They are obtained from roots, buds, flowers, fruits, bark or seeds.
Uses: Spices enhance countless dishes if used appropriately. When using a spice for the first time it is best to start with ⅛ teaspoon and increase the amount gradually according to taste.
Storage: Store spices in an airtight container in a cool, dark, dry place. Whole spices will keep for up to two years, ground spices for up to 6 months. Most spices are good sources of antioxidants.

Allspice

Allspice is a small pea-size berry, dried to a reddish brown color. It has a flavor and aroma similar to a blend of cloves, cinnamon and nutmeg.
Uses: Allspice is used whole in pickling and cooking meats and in fish and patés. Use it ground to add zest to stews, tomato sauces, marinades, relishes and preserves, cooked fruit, puddings, cakes and other baked items.

Anise

Anise is the small dried ripe fruit of an annual herb in the parsley family. It has a licorice-like flavor.
Uses: Use anise in cakes, cookies, candies and breads. Add anise to pickles, cole slaw and ground pork.

Caper

Capers are the small buds of a Mediterranean bush. They are pickled in vinegar or dried and salted. Capers have a firm, almost crunchy texture.
Uses: Capers are delicious in sauces, dressings and salads such as green salads and potato salads. They are especially good with eggs, seafood such as smoked salmon and as a garnish for fish or veal.

Caraway Seed
This hard brown spiky seed from a plant in the parsley family has a pungent, slightly sweet flavor.
Uses: Caraway seeds are most often associated with rye bread. Add it to noodles, cheeses, cooked cabbage, sauerkraut, cole slaw and meats such as goose and pork.

Cardamom
Cardamom is the dried fruit of a tropical bush in the ginger family. The fragrant, hard black seeds are encased in a small round pod. Cardamom is quite aromatic and pungent.
Uses: Use cardamom in applesauce and baked apples, poached fruits, fruit pies, cookies, breads, cakes, and preserves. Add it to curries, stews, rice pilafs and braised meat dishes. Cardamom is also used to flavor coffee.

Cayenne Pepper
Cayenne pepper is finely ground small hot red capsicum peppers. When fresh it is quite hot.
Uses: Use it in eggs, fish, vegetables, meats, stews, sauces, salad dressings, soups, curries, chutneys and chili. Use cayenne sparingly as a little bit goes a long way.

Celery Seed
The seedlike fruit of wild celery, celery seed has a pungent flavor reminiscent of celery.
Uses: Add it to potato salad, aromatic vegetables, soups, salad dressings, salads, pickling mixtures, tomato juice, cole slaw, stuffings, meat and fish dishes.

Chili Powder
Chili powder consists of ground chili pepper pods and blended spices. This spice has a very hot flavor.
Uses: Use in making chili and other Mexican dishes.

Cinnamon
The dried inner bark of the cinnamon tree, cinnamon is the most popular baking spice in America.
Uses: Use it in stick form in mulled winter drinks, hot cocoa, fruits and preserves. Use ground cinnamon in cakes, cookies, pies, puddings, sweet rolls, muffins, breads, rice pudding, and pastries. It can be used in beef stews, ground lamb dishes and carrot salads.

Clove
The dried flower buds of the clove

tree, clove is extremely aromatic with a sweet, peppery flavor.
Uses: Use whole in meats such as baked ham, soups, stews, to stud onions for flavoring stock, with fish and in pickling. Add whole cloves to mulled hot cider or hot cocoa. Ground clove adds a wonderful flavor to cakes, gingerbread, fruit pies, cookies, puddings, fruit compote and baked fruit.

Coriander

Coriander spice is the dried ripe fruit of an herb of the parsley family.
Uses: Use whole seeds in pickling and making aromatic vegetables, poultry stuffing and green salads. Use ground in baking gingerbread, coffee cakes, Danish pastry, cookies, in sausages, and lamb, pork, chicken and cheese dishes. It is often an ingredient in curry powder. Coriander contains active botanical factors with anticancer activity.

Cumin Seed

Cumin is the tiny dried aromatic fruit of a plant in the parsley family. The seed resembles caraway and its aroma and flavor are quite sharp, spicy and pungent.
Uses: Cumin is used whole in soups, stews, cheeses, egg dishes

and sausage. Ground, it is a common ingredient in curry and chili powders.

Curry

Curry is not a single spice but a blend of turmeric, cumin, coriander, fenugreek, red peppers and other pungent spices.
Uses: Use curry powder in curries, eggs, and tuna and chicken salads.

Dill Seed

The small, dark seed of the dill plant, dill seed has a warm, slightly bitter sharp flavor similar to caraway seed.
Uses: Dill seed is an ingredient of most pickling mixtures. Use it in breads, sauerkraut, cole slaw, salads, soups, sauces and stews.

Fennel Seed

This small, yellowish brown seed has a licorice like flavor.
Uses: Use fennel seed in aromatic vegetables, fish soups, breads, sausages, pork roasts, stuffings and apple pie. In India it is served after dinner as a breath freshener and digestive.

Fenugreek

Fenugreek spice is made from the small, yellow-brown fenugreek seeds that have been dried and roasted.

Uses: Fenugreek is an important ingredient of curry powder blends. It is also used to flavor imitation syrup. It can be used to season stews, chutneys and breads.

Ground Ginger

Dried ground powder of the ginger root, this spice has a wonderful sweet/hot flavor.

Uses: Use ground ginger in baking cakes, cookies, puddings and quick breads. Use it in pot roasts, chickpea and lentil soups, couscous, stews, carrots, beets, winter squashes, baked fruits and fruit cobblers. Ginger is an appetite stimulant.

Juniper Berry

Juniper berries are the small, round, bluish black berries of wild European evergreen shrubs. These berries are highly aromatic.

Uses: Juniper berries give gin its characteristic taste. They are also used in marinades and sauces for meat and game.

Mace

Mace is the orange-red skin surrounding the shell of the nutmeg kernel. The mace is separated from the nutmeg and ground separately or broken into flakes. Mace has a sweeter, lighter, milder flavor than the nutmeg it conceals.

Uses: Use flaked mace in fish sauces, pickling, preserving, and in clear soups. Use ground mace in pound cakes and other cakes, cookies, pies, puddings and chocolate dishes. It may also be used in curries.

Mustard

Mustard seeds are the small round seeds of a plant which bears yellow flowers. There are three types of mustard seed: yellow, brown, and black. Yellow seed is used to make yellow mustards. The more pungent brown seed is used to make Dijon-style mustards. Powdered mustard consists of a mixture of yellow and brown seeds. The slightly milder black seed is used in Indian cooking.

Uses: When moistened with water or other liquid and allowed to sit for 10 minutes, ground mustard becomes quite hot. Make prepared mustard from ground mustard seeds and use for sandwiches, sausages, cold cuts and cold meats. Mix with salad dressings, mayonnaise and sauces.

Nutmeg

Nutmeg is the kernel of the nutmeg fruit. When grated it is quite aromatic with a slightly bitter flavor.

Uses: Ground nutmeg loses its flavor quickly so it is best to buy whole nutmeg and grate it at home when needed with a hand grater. Nutmeg is a wonderful baking spice used in cakes, donuts, puddings, pumpkin and custard pies, sweet breads and cookies. Add it to eggnog. Use nutmeg in cheese sauces and dishes, winter squashes, spinach, potatoes and sausages.

Paprika

Paprika is a ground spice derived from dried, ripe red capsicum peppers. The peppers used to make paprika determine its various colors and pungency. Paprika has a pleasant odor and a flavor that ranges from mild and sweet to hot. Paprika is an excellent source of Vitamin C.

Uses: Use paprika to season and color baked fish, shellfish, salad dressings, canapé spreads, cheese and vegetable casseroles. Use it in sausages and condiments, soups, stews, salads and rice dishes.

Pepper

Peppercorns are small round berries that change from green to yellow to red as they ripen on the vine. Black peppercorns are berries that were picked slightly underripe, then sundried until blackened and shriveled. White peppercorns are the same peppercorns that have been picked when ripe and hulled. White peppercorns are less pungent than black. Green peppercorns are soft, underripe berries that have not been dried. Pink peppercorns are pungent berries unrelated to black, white, and green peppercorns.

Uses: Use whole peppercorns when pickling, meats and stews but crush them slightly first or they won't release any flavor. Ground pepper is used to season countless dishes: meats, fish, poultry, vegetables, salads, pastas, sauces, and soups to name a few. Milder white pepper is often used for fish or light-colored sauces. Use green and pink peppercorns to season meats and fish.

Poppy Seed

These tiny, dark gray seeds of the poppy plant have a slightly sweet, nutty flavor.

Uses: Poppy seeds are used to top breads and rolls and as fillings for buns and pastries. Use them in cakes and salad dressings and tossed with noodles.

Saffron

Saffron is the most expensive spice in the world. It is made from the dried stigma of a species of crocus. It gives a beautiful yellow color and delicate flavor to various dishes.

Uses: Buy saffron in threads rather than ground. Saffron threads must first be steeped in hot liquid to bring out their flavor. Use saffron in paella and other rice dishes, risotto, fish soups, couscous, curries, pilafs and tandoori dishes. It can be added to breads, cakes, and buns, and to chicken and noodle dishes and soups.

Sesame Seed

These small, flat, oily seeds of the sesame plant can be found in white and black varieties. Sesame seeds have a nutty, slightly sweet flavor that intensifies when the seeds are toasted.

Uses: Use sesame seeds when making rolls, breads, cookies, candies, pilafs, stuffings, sauces, pasta dishes, noodle dishes, stir-fries, chicken salad, meatballs, mixed vegetables, as a coating for fried foods and sprinkled over meat and poultry. Good source of Vitamin E.

Turmeric

Turmeric is a spice made from the ground, dried, aromatic root of the turmeric plant. Turmeric has a yellow color and pungent, slightly bitter flavor.

Uses: Turmeric is an important ingredient in curry powder blends. Use it to season meat, egg, and rice dishes. Turmeric contains botanical factors with anti cancer activity.

FISH

*NOTE: All fish listed is cooked without added fat unless otherwise indicated.

LEAN OR LOW-FAT FISH

	PORTION	CALORIES	FAT (grams)	% CAL FROM FAT
-Sea Bass	3 oz.	05	2.1	18
-Halibut	3 oz.	20	2.4	18
-Rockfish	3 oz.	02	1.8	16
-Red Snapper	3 oz.	08	1.5	12
-Flounder	3 oz.	99	1.2	11
-Grouper	3 oz.	99	1.2	11
-Sole	3 oz.	80	1.0	11
-Whiting	3 oz.	98	1.0	9
-Pike	3 oz.	96	1.0	9
-Haddock	3 oz.	96	0.9	8
-Perch	3 oz.	99	0.9	8
-Cod, Ling Cod	3 oz.	90	0.6	6

Best cooking methods:
Lean fish have a delicate, mild flavor and light-colored, firm flesh. These varieties are best when cooked with additional fats or liquids since their lean flesh can dry out easily. Poach, steam, deep-fry, pan-fry, bake, or broil lean fish.

MEDIUM-FAT OR OILY FISH

	PORTION	CALORIES	FAT (grams)	% CAL FROM FAT
-Mackerel	3 oz.	222	15.0	61
-Shad	3 oz.	167	11.5	62
-Pompano	3 oz.	180	10.2	51
-Herring	3 oz.	134	8.0	54
-Salmon	3 oz.	157	6.0	34
-Shark	3 oz.	111	4.0	32
-Swordfish	3 oz.	132	4.5	31
-Tuna (bluefin)	3 oz.	156	5.0	29
-Trout (rainbow)	3 oz.	129	3.6	25

Cured/Smoked Fish

Both finfish and shellfish can be found smoked, salted, dried and marinated. Examples include smoked whitefish, kippered salmon, salted cod and pickled herring. Fish is salted in either brine or dry salt. Salted fish is then smoked for a short time to make smoked fish. Oily fish are preserved in this way.

Best cooking methods:

Medium-fat fish are richer and have a stronger flavor and darker flesh. These types of fish are best grilled, baked, and broiled.

SHELLFISH

	PORTION	CALORIES	FAT (grams)	% CAL FROM FAT
-Oysters (raw)	3.5 oz.	76	2.0	24
-Mussels	3.5 oz.	95	2.0	19
-Crab (Blue)	3 oz.	87	1.5	15
-Clams (raw)	3 oz.	63	1.0	14
-Clams (cooked)	3 oz.	126	1.8	13
-Crab (Alaskan King)	3 oz.	81	1.2	13
-Crayfish	3 oz.	96	1.2	11
-Scallops	3.5 oz.	81	1.0	11
-Crab (Dungeness)	3 oz.	94	1.0	10
-Crab (Imitation-Surimi)	3 oz.	87	1.0	10
-Shrimp	3 oz.	84	0.9	10
-Lobster	3 oz.	84	0.6	6

Best cooking method:
Most shellfish can be grilled, steamed, baked, sautéed, poached, stir-fried or deep-fried.

Buying fresh fish:

It is best to buy fresh fish the day you will cook it. Fresh fish should have a mild smell, not a fishy one. The flesh should be firm and glistening. If there is skin on the fish it should be tight and scales should be shimmering and firmly attached. Be sure the eyes of the fish are clear, shiny and bulging and the gills are a reddish-pink.

Storing fresh fish:

Fish spoils quickly and should be used as soon as possible after it is bought. Store fresh fish in the coldest part of the refrigerator (lower shelves) for no more than two days. Store fish either wrapped in wax paper and placed in a covered container or wrapped in aluminum foil or plastic wrap.

Buying frozen fish:

The flesh of frozen fish should be solid and shiny with no signs of freezer burn or drying when you buy it. There should be little or no aroma. Be sure the fish is tight and moistureproof with no frost or ice crystals inside.

Storing frozen fish:

Store frozen fish at 0 degrees F. (-18° C.) or colder to prevent loss of color, flavor, texture and nutritive value. Store medium-fat or oily fish for a maximum of two months and lean fish for a maximum of six months.

COOKING FISH

COOKING TIME:

Determine cooking time by measuring fish at the thickest part, whether or not it is stuffed. Cook 10 minutes per inch of thickness for fresh fish, 20 minutes per inch for frozen fish. If cooking fish in foil, add five minutes for fresh, 10 for frozen. Fish is cooked when flesh is opaque and falls easily into clumps of flakes when tested with a fork.

STEAMING (STOVETOP):

Fill a steamer pot with two inches of water. Bring to the boil. Season the fish, wrap in cheesecloth if necessary if the fish is delicate, and place on steamer rack above boiling water. Cover and cook for appropriate amount of time with the water hardly bubbling.

STEAMING (OVEN IN FOIL):

Preheat oven to 450° F. Place fish on lightly greased foil.

Season and sprinkle with white wine and/or lemon juice. Wrap securely and bake on a baking sheet for the appropriate length of time.

POACHING:

Bring water, court bouillon, or fish stock to a boil. Season fish and wrap in cheesecloth. Place in boiling liquid cover pan and return to a boil. Reduce heat and simmer for required cooking time.

MICROWAVING:

Place fish in a microwave-proof dish. Cover with plastic wrap leaving some space for steam to escape. Microwave on high for three to four minutes per pound. Let stand two to three minutes.

MEAT

There are several grades of beef, veal, lamb and pork, depending on the marbling of fat within the flesh and with age. The highest grade is called USDA Prime and is generally reserved for restaurants and specialty shops. Prime cuts have more marbling which dissolves during cooking making the meat more juicy. Most of what you find in the supermarket is Choice and Select. Choice is more tender and juicy but Select is fine for cuts of meat that require long, slow cooking. Meat is generally categorized as tender or less tender depending on which part of the animal the cut is from. Tender cuts come from the least worked sections of the animal. Less tender cuts come from the more exercised, muscular parts. Tender cuts are usually best cooked by dry heat methods such as roasting, baking, grilling, broiling, pan frying and stir-frying. Less tender cuts are best cooked by moist heat methods such as braising and stewing.

Storing meat: Unless you plan on using the meat on the day you buy it, remove it from its original package, put it on a plate and cover it with plastic wrap. Store in the coldest part of the refrigerator. To store in the freezer, remove the meat from its original wrapping, then cover with plastic wrap and freezer wrap on top.

Beef

Cut of beef and best cooking method: (See also page 41)

Tender portions: Rib, Delmonico, club, porterhouse,

NUTRITIONAL VALUES FOR LEAN MEATS AND POULTRY

(per 100 grams)

Type of Meat	Calories	Fat	Saturated fat(g)	Cholesterol (mg)	Protein (g)	Iron (mg)	Zinc (mg)	Vitamin B1 (mg)	Vitamin B2 (mg)	Niacin (mg)	Vitamin B6 (mg)
BEEF											
Lean	186	7	2	89	30.4	0.4	6.5	0.1	0.3	4	0.5
Medium	214	11	3	96	31.6	3.5	5.5	0.1	0.3	4	0.4
LAMB											
Lean	180	8	2	87	28.2	2	4.1	0.1	6.6	0.3	2.5
PORK											
Lean	170	8	2	48	24.9	1	3	0.7	0.2	5	0.4
VEAL	172	8	3	103	24.4	1	4	0.1	0.3	8	0.4
ORGAN MEATS											
Liver	165	7	2	389	24.4	6.8	6	0.2	4.1	11	1
Tongue	283	21	9	107	22.1	3.4	4.8	0.03	0.4	2	0.2
POULTRY											
Chicken Dark meat	205	10	3	93	27.4	1.4	2.7	0.06	0.2	5	0.2
Light meat	173	5	1	85	30.9	1.1	1.2	0.07	0.1	12	0.6
TURKEY											
Dark meat	221	12	3.5	89	27.5	2.3	4.2	0.06	0.2	4	0.3
Light meat	157	3	1	69	29.9	1.4	2	0.06	0.1	7	0.5

T-bone, sirloin, New York strip and filet mignon steaks. These are best grilled, broiled, pan-fried or stir-fried. Rib, top round, top sirloin and tenderloin are best roasted.

Less tender portions: Brisket, chuck, shoulder, cross-rib, rump, bottom round and plate. These cuts are best stewed, pot roasted or braised.

Ground beef: Varieties of ground beef differ in the amount of fat they contain. The varieties in order of increasing fat content are: Ground sirloin, ground round, ground chuck, and ground beef. Round or chuck are best for making hamburgers as some fat is needed in the meat to give it flavor and juiciness and to hold the burgers together. Sirloin is best for things such as chili and meat sauces for pasta. Ground beef generally has too much fat to be recommended.

Buying beef: Look for bright pink-red flesh with tiny flecks of creamy-white fat. Avoid meat that has brownish streaks or dark spots.

Storing beef: Larger cuts of meat such as roasts will keep in the refrigerator for three to four days and in the freezer for six to nine months. Steaks can be refrigerated for two to three days and in the freezer for six months. Kebabs and stew meat will be good for two days in the refrigerator and three months in the freezer. Ground beef should only be stored in the refrigerator for a maximum of one day after purchase. It may be frozen for up to three months.

Veal

Veal is the meat of young calves. Milk-fed veal comes from calves that were slaughtered when they were less than six months old and were not yet weaned. This type of veal is white, tender and mildly flavored. It is also expensive. Veal has very little fat and becomes dry if not cooked properly.

Buying veal: Veal should be a light pinkish-cream color. Milk fed veal will be whiter than veal from animals that have been allowed to graze. The iron in the grass gives the flesh a pinkish red color. Avoid veal that has a deep, reddish hue as this is an indication that the meat is too old, in other words, is beef.

Storing veal: Store large veal roasts and chops in the

CUTS OF BEEF

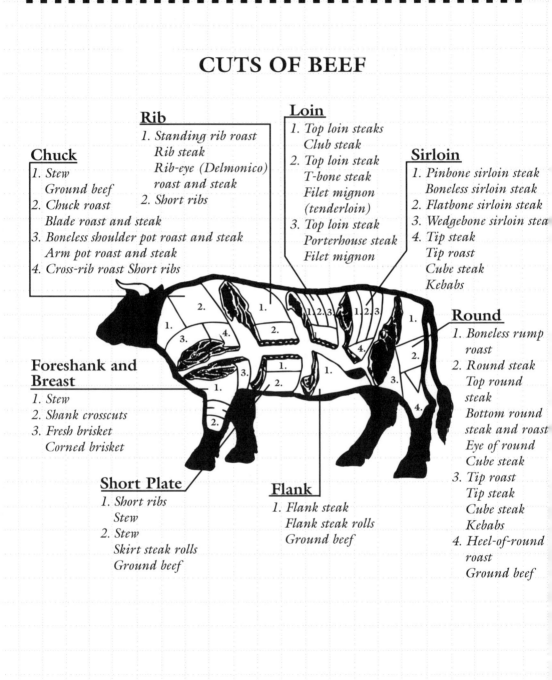

Rib
1. Standing rib roast
   Rib steak
   Rib-eye (Delmonico)
   roast and steak
2. Short ribs

Loin
1. Top loin steaks
   Club steak
2. Top loin steak
   T-bone steak
   Filet mignon
   (tenderloin)
3. Top loin steak
   Porterhouse steak
   Filet mignon

Chuck
1. Stew
   Ground beef
2. Chuck roast
   Blade roast and steak
3. Boneless shoulder pot roast and steak
   Arm pot roast and steak
4. Cross-rib roast Short ribs

Sirloin
1. Pinbone sirloin steak
   Boneless sirloin steak
2. Flatbone sirloin steak
3. Wedgebone sirloin steak
4. Tip steak
   Tip roast
   Cube steak
   Kebabs

Foreshank and Breast
1. Stew
2. Shank crosscuts
3. Fresh brisket
   Corned brisket

Round
1. Boneless rump
   roast
2. Round steak
   Top round
   steak
   Bottom round
   steak and roast
   Eye of round
   Cube steak
3. Tip roast
   Tip steak
   Cube steak
   Kebabs
4. Heel-of-round
   roast
   Ground beef

Short Plate
1. Short ribs
   Stew
2. Stew
   Skirt steak rolls
   Ground beef

Flank
1. Flank steak
   Flank steak rolls
   Ground beef

refrigerator for up to three days; cutlets for two days; ground veal for no more than one day. All cuts other than ground veal can be stored in the freezer for up to six months. Store ground veal for no more than two months.

Most tender portions: Loin and rib. These are best broiled, grilled, or pan-fried as chops, or roasted as larger pieces.

Less tender portions: Boneless shoulder can be roasted but must be basted often. Shank is best braised and the leg (round and rump) should be braised or roasted.

Veal cutlets: Steaks cut from the leg of the calf and pounded to tenderness. These are best pan-fried or grilled and are often first coated with beaten egg and breaded to retain the moisture.

Lamb

Lamb is the meat from young sheep that were slaughtered at less than one year old. The meat from older sheep, rarely seen in American stores, is called mutton.

Buying lamb: Look for bright pink flesh, white fat, and pink bones. Older lamb has dark red meat and bones.

Storing lamb: Store large lamb portions in the refrigerator for three to four days and in the freezer for eight to nine months. Refrigerate chops, shanks, stew, and kebabs for two to three days or freeze for four to six months. Store ground lamb in the refrigerator for no more than one day and in the freezer for one to two months.

Cuts of lamb and the best cooking method:

Most tender portions: Loin and rib chops are best broiled, grilled, or pan-fried. Loin and rib can also be made into a crown roast shaped in a circle and garnished with paper caps on the tips of each cutler bone. Leg of lamb is best roasted and butterflied leg of lamb, which is boneless and slightly flattened, can be grilled or broiled.

Less tender portions: Spareribs and breast are less expensive cuts and of lamb and should be roasted or braised.

Least tender portions: Shoulder roast, shanks, and neck meat are best braised or stewed.

Pork

Fresh pork is a good source of B vitamins and protein and is

CUTS OF LAMB

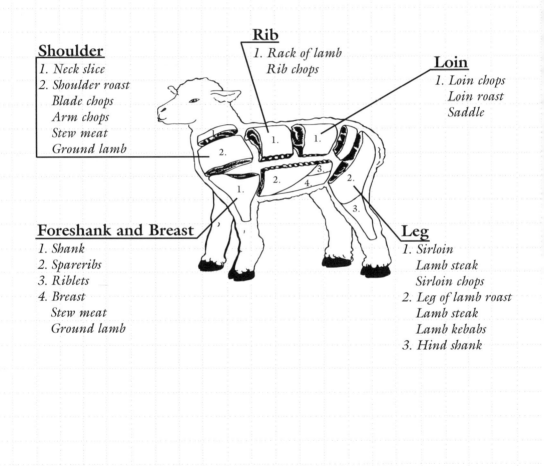

Rib
1. Rack of lamb
Rib chops

Shoulder
1. Neck slice
2. Shoulder roast
Blade chops
Arm chops
Stew meat
Ground lamb

Loin
1. Loin chops
Loin roast
Saddle

Foreshank and Breast
1. Shank
2. Spareribs
3. Riblets
4. Breast
Stew meat
Ground lamb

Leg
1. Sirloin
Lamb steak
Sirloin chops
2. Leg of lamb roast
Lamb steak
Lamb kebabs
3. Hind shank

flavorful. Unfortunately, pork is often overcooked in an effort to make it safe to eat. As long as the meat reaches an internal temperature of between 140° F and 160° F, it is safe from tapeworm larvae and will still be succulent.

Cuts of pork and the best cooking method:

Most portions of pork are tender enough for dry heat methods such as baking, broiling, and roasting.

Pork tenderloin can be grilled, roasted, pan-fried, or stir-fried.

Loin and rib chops can be grilled, broiled or pan-fried. Double-thick ones, pork loin roast and crown roast are best roasted.

Spareribs and sausages are good grilled, broiled, or baked.

Fresh ham or leg of pork, picnic roasts from the arm, and Boston butt from the shoulder should be roasted or braised.

Buying pork: Look for light pink to white meat, pink bones and white fat.

Storing pork: Keep large cuts of pork in the refrigerator for up to three days; chops, sausage and spareribs for two days; ground pork for one day.

Freeze roasts for up to six months; chops and sausage for 3 months; ground pork, bacon and hot dogs for one to two months.

POULTRY AND GAME BIRDS

Poultry and game birds include chicken, turkey, duck, goose, Rock Cornish game hen, poussin, squab and quail.

Buying poultry and game birds: The color of the bird does not indicate its quality but varies according to what the bird has been fed. Look for birds with moist skin and avoid those with visible pinfeathers and long hairs or an off-aroma. Avoid packages of chicken with lots of runny red liquid.

When buying frozen poultry, avoid birds with signs of freezer burn (pinkish colored ice) or torn packages.

Storing poultry and game birds: Whole birds will keep in the refrigerator for two to three days; parts for one to two days. Both whole birds and parts may be frozen for up to eight months. Because poultry is so perishable, take it straight home from the market. Prepackaged poultry can be refrigerated in its original packaging. If the wrapping is torn, or if it is wrapped in butcher paper, rinse thoroughly in cold water and rewrap loosely before refrigerating. To freeze fresh or frozen poultry, wrap tightly in plastic wrap and then in freezer wrap

Chicken

Chicken is classified by its age and weight.

Classification of chicken and best cooking method:

Broilers-fryers are young birds between seven to eight weeks old which weigh from 2 ½ to four pounds. They may be cut up into separate parts or sold whole. Whether cut-up or whole, broilers-fryers are best grilled, broiled, pan-fried, deep-fried, or poached.

Roasters are two to six weeks older than fryers and generally weigh between 4 ½ and eight pounds. These should be roasted as the name implies.

Stewing hens are older and tougher. They require slow cooking with moist heat such as braising. Stewing hens are great for making soup and stock.

Capons are young, castrated male chickens. The sweet, tender meat of capons is best roasted.

Rock Cornish Hens are tiny chickens that weigh about one pound. They may be roasted, grilled or pan-fried.

Turkey

Turkey comes in various weights and may be bought whole or in parts as well as ground. Fryer-roasters weigh four to eight pounds and young hens weigh seven to fifteen pounds. Fully mature hens weigh up to 30 pounds. Turkey is generally best roasted.

Other birds

Domestic ducklings weigh three to four pounds and are best broiled or roasted on a rack to drain off excess fat.

Mature ducks weigh five to six pounds and should be roasted or braised.

Goose weighs from four to 16 pounds and should be roasted on a rack to drain off excess fat.

Pheasants weigh two to three pounds and should be baked or roasted and basted well.

Quail weighs ¼ to ½ pound and may be either broiled, grilled, roasted, or sautéed.

Squab weighs ¾ pound and may be broiled, grilled, roasted, or sautéed.

VARIETY MEATS

Variety meats are the internal organs and extremities of meat animals. They include brains, chitterlings, ears, feet, testicles, gizzard, heart, kidney, liver, sweetbreads, tail, tongue and tripe. Variety meats are generally high in protein, minerals and iron.

Storage: Variety meats are highly perishable. If purchased fresh, variety meats should be refrigerated, loosely wrapped and used within 24 hours. Loose wrapping allows air to circulate around the meat, drying its surface and retarding bacterial growth. If purchased frozen, they may be stored in the freezer for up to three months.

Liver

Liver is the most commonly used variety meat in the United States. Liver has a smooth texture and rich flavor. Calves' liver is the most tender and flavorful. Beef liver is also good but has a tougher texture and stronger flavor. Pork liver has a stronger flavor and aroma. Pork and goose livers are generally used for making patés. Chicken, duck, turkey and goose livers are very tender and flavorful.

What to look for: Liver should have a bright, shiny surface and be firm and moist.

Preparation: Remove the outer membrane if the butcher has not yet done so. Trim away any visible fat and connective tissue and wipe the liver clean with a paper towel. Liver should never be overcooked as it quickly becomes tough and dry. Livers may be roasted, sautéd stir-fried, or made into a mousse, paté, or chopped liver.

Tongue

Tongue is available fresh, pickled, and smoked. Beef and veal tongue are the most commonly available. Lamb and pork tongues are small, delicious, and harder to find. Tongue has a rich flavor and firm, meaty texture.

What to look for: Beef, veal, lamb, and pork tongue should be firm and fresh-looking with no rancid smell.

Preparation: Prepare fresh tongues by first scrubbing them with a brush in warm running water, then soaking them in cold water for one to two hours. Poach in court bouillon until tender: three to four hours for beef tongue, 1 ½ to two hours for veal, one to 1 ½ hours for pork, and 1 hour for lamb. Drain and cool. Then peel off skin and trim away fat, gristle, and any small bones. Place in a bowl and cover with a plate and place a heavy weight on top. Leave overnight for "pressed" tongue. Tongue may be used in a variety of ways. It may be served hot or cold with sauce, or braised or baked with herbs and vegetables. Pickled or smoked tongue may be sliced and used in sandwiches.

SMOKED AND CURED MEATS
Ham:

Ham is made from pork hind legs. Ham is cured in a variety of ways; it may be soaked with a brine seasoned with spices or with a dry salt mixture. After brining or salting, the ham may be smoked and/or air-dried.

Canned ham is commonly made by immersing the meat in a brine while at the same time injecting it with the brine to speed the curing process. After curing, the ham is usually smoked. The hams are then fully or partially cooked.

Preparation: Hams labeled "ready-to-eat" and "fully cooked" do not need further

cooking, but may be heated. Hams labeled "heat-and-serve" should be baked until the internal temperature reaches 150°.

Storage: Canned hams should always be refrigerated after opening and even before opening unless labeled "sterilized."

Smithfield, Virginia and other country-type ham are often made by salting the leg for about four weeks, then washing it, coating it with peppercorns and refrigerating it for about two weeks, then smoking it for about ten days. The meat is then aged for six to twelve months.

Preparation: Ham is very salty and may be eaten raw, usually in very thin slices.

To cook, first soak the ham for 12 to 24 hours in several changes of cold water then scrub with a stiff brush. Cover in cold water, bring to a boil and simmer until the small bone near the shank feels loose. Slice away ham rind. The ham may then be glazed and baked.

Storage: Store wrapped in the refrigerator.

Prosciutto is Italian-style salted and air-dried ham.

Preparation: Prosciutto

should generally not be cooked.
It may be eaten raw, thinly sliced
or it may be stirred into cooked
dishes at the end of cooking.

Storage: Store wrapped in
the refrigerator.

Canadian Bacon

Canadian bacon is lean pork loin
that has been cured and smoked.
It is more like ham than bacon in
both appearance and flavor.

Preparation: Canadian
bacon comes ready to eat and
can be purchased packaged and
either whole or sliced. Whole
Canadian bacons can be baked
and glazed like ham. Sliced it can
be pan-fried and eaten with eggs.

Storage: Store Canadian
bacon in the refrigerator for
three to four days or in the
freezer, tightly wrapped, for up
to a month.

CHEESE

When milk coagulates, it
separates into solid curds, cheese
and liquid whey. Milk is first
coagulated by adding either
bacteria or enzymes that cause it
to curdle.

The numerous varieties of
cheese result from variations in
the source and type of milk
used, the treatment after

coagulation, the cultures used
and the aging process. Most
cheeses are made from either
cow's, sheep's or goat's milk.
Cheeses may be made from
whole or skimmed milk, a
combination of the two or milk
and cream. It may be made from
pasteurized or unpasteurized
(raw) milk.

After coagulation, the curd is
cut into smaller pieces and the
whey drained. The texture and
moisture content of the finished
cheese is determined by the size
of the cut and the length of the
draining period. The smaller the
cut and the longer the draining
period, the firmer the cheese. The
curds are then molded and some
are also pressed which makes
them even firmer. After they are
molded, cheeses may be soaked in
brine or washed repeatedly with
water, brine or alcohol. They may
be waxed, smoked, covered with
herbs or leaves, coated with ashes
or soaked in oil.

Cheeses may then be aged or
ripened. This process develops
flavor and causes moisture loss.
The longer it is aged, the
stronger a cheese's flavor and
the drier its texture.
Cheeses are classified as soft

unripened cheese, soft ripened cheese, semisoft cheese, semifirm cheese, and firm cheese.

Soft unripened cheese

These cheeses, also known as fresh cheeses, are made from cream or a mixture of milk, skim milk, and concentrated skim milk. They undergo little or no ripening. These cheeses are usually very creamy and mild.

Examples: Cottage, Cream, Pot, Ricotta, Mozzarella, Farmer, and Neufchatel cheeses as well as the French Fromage blanc.

Uses: Cream cheese is delicious as a spread for bread or crackers. Cottage and pot cheeses may be eaten with vegetables or fruit. Fresh cheeses are also used to make cheesecakes.

What to look for: Choose only very fresh soft unripened cheeses as they are quite perishable.

Storage: These cheeses are highly perishable because of their moisture content. They should be stored in the refrigerator in a covered container for no more than a week.

Soft-ripened cheese

These cheeses are not cooked or pressed. They are cut into large curds and allowed to drain naturally. Mold or bacteria are then used to ripen the cheeses. These cheeses develop a rind and ripen from the rind inward. Soft-ripened cheeses have a smooth, soft texture and range in flavor from strong to mild.

Examples: Boursault, Brie, Camembert, Liederkranz and Limburger.

Uses: These cheeses are often served at dinner after the main course but before dessert. They are generally served with crackers, bread, and wine. Soft-ripened cheeses should be served at room temperature. Their rinds are edible but may be cut away.

What to look for: Choose soft-ripened cheeses that yield slightly to pressure but are not liquidy. Look for those with an evenly colored, slightly moist rind. Avoid any that have a strong aroma of ammonia, which means they are overripe, or that have a chalky white center, which means they are underripe.

Storage: Wrap airtight in plastic and store in the refrigerator for a couple of weeks. Change the plastic wrapping every few days.

Semisoft ripened cheese

These cheeses are usually pressed but uncooked. They range in flavor from mild to strong, and in texture from soft to firm and crumbly. These cheeses are ripened either by bacteria or by mold. The mold-ripened cheeses in this category are called blue-vein cheeses.

Examples: Bel Paese, Brick, Esrom, Fontina, Gouda, Havarti, Jack, Muenster, Port du Salut, Tilsit, Blue, Gorgonzola, Roquefort and Stilton.

Uses: These cheeses are usually served with crackers, bread, and wine. The soft, sliceable cheeses may be used for sandwiches, melted or not or melted on top of a casserole. The blue-veined cheeses are delicious with fruit and nuts. They may be crumbled into salads or whipped with butter as a topping for grilled meat or crackers. Serve semisoft ripened cheeses at room temperature.

What to look for: Choose cheeses with a strong but not rank or ammonia-like aroma.

Storage: Store cheese in the refrigerator, wrapped airtight in plastic, for up to a month. Change the wrapping every few days.

Semifirm ripened cheese

These cheeses have been cooked and pressed. They are ripened with bacteria and may or may not have a rind. They are ripened from two months to one year and the flavor becomes increasingly sharp. They have a firm texture but are smooth enough to be sliced.

Examples: Appenzeller, Asagio, Cheddar, Cheshire, Colby, Edam, Emmentaler, Gjetost, Gruyére, Jarlsberg, Provolone, Sap Sago and Swiss.

Uses: Serve these cheeses with crackers, bread and wine. They may be sliced onto sandwiches. Most can be grated and melted in cooked dishes such as omelets, soufflés, casseroles, breads, puddings and pies.

What to look for: Chooses cheeses that have smooth, uncracked rinds. Avoid those with a dry, crumbly texture.

Storage: Store in the refrigerator, wrapped airtight in plastic, changing the wrapping every few days. For long storage, wrap in aluminum foil as well. They will last for several months. These cheeses may also be frozen for up to two months wrapped in plastic and then foil.

Defrost slowly in the refrigerator.

Firm ripened cheese

These cheeses have been cooked and pressed, then aged until dry and hard. These cheeses can be sliced when they are young but must be grated when aged. These cheeses have been aged for at least six months and most are aged for over a year.

Examples: Aged Asagio, Parmesan, Romano and Sapsago.

Uses: These cheeses are made for grating, unless young. They are delicious in soups, salads, casseroles, pizzas and in rice or egg dishes.

What to look for: Firm ripened cheeses go stale quickly after grating so it is best to buy blocks of these cheeses and grate them just before using. Choose cheeses that are hard but not dried out.

Storage: Wrap in airtight plastic and store in the refrigerator for several months. Change the wrapping every few days. For longer storage, wrap in aluminum foil as well. These cheeses may be frozen for up to two months wrapped in plastic and then foil. Defrost slowly in the refrigerator.

Pasteurized Processed Cheese

This is one or more kinds of natural cheese that have been ground up, blended and heated with an emulsifying agent to make it uniformly smooth. The heat used in the processing prevents further aging and subsequent flavor changes from taking place. The flavor will remain unchanged for several months.

Pasteurized Processed Cheese Food

Pasteurized processed cheese foods are produced by the addition of certain dairy products (such as cream, milk, buttermilk, whey) to processed cheese. Processed cheese food has more water and less protein and fat than processed cheese.

Pasteurized Processed Cheese Spread

These have a higher moisture content and lower fat content than processed cheese food. The protein content is only about two-thirds as much as in processed cheese.

Uses of processed cheeses: These cheeses melt smoothly and evenly and are often used in cooking.

Storage: Processed cheeses

keep well and are usually conveniently packaged. Follow storage directions on package.

GRAINS

Grains are grasses that bear edible seeds. Both the plant and the seed are called grain. The seeds are the fruit of the grain. As a complete fruit, a seed contains all of the equipment needed for reproduction and is the most nutritious part of the plant. The outermost layer of grain is called the husk or hull. It is hard and inedible. Bran is the protective covering on the grain. Bran is high in minerals, B vitamins and dietary fiber. The bran layer encloses the endosperm and the embryo or germ. The endosperm is the starchy center of the grain. It is high in carbohydrates. White rice and pearled barley are examples of endosperms. The germ is the part of the kernel that produces the sprout. It is rich in enzymes, protein, fat and vitamins and minerals.

Polished grains have had both the bran and the germ removed. They are thus much lower in nutritive value than whole grains.

Storage: The germ of whole grains contain oils that can turn rancid. Cracked grains become rancid even more quickly because the oily germ is exposed. Buy whole or cracked grains in small quantities and store in the refrigerator in an airtight container for up to six months to avoid rancidity. If stored at room temperature, whole grains will only last up to a month. Polished kernels, that have the bran and germ removed, have a longer shelf life. Store them in a cool, dry spot in an airtight container for up to a year.

Barley

Barley is milled to remove its hull. The more times the milling process or pearling is repeated, the more refined is the grain. Pot barley has been pearled three times and still retains some of its bran. Most barley is pearled five or six times yielding pearl barley which has neither hull, bran, nor germ.

Uses: Barley's major uses are for animal feed and to make malt for beer. Barley is delicious in soups and stews, as a side dish, as a breakfast cereal, in a pilaf, with meat and game and cooked with vegetables, beans and nuts.

Nutritional Analysis: Pot barley is a good source of Niacin, Thiamin, Potassium, Iron, Phosphorous, Calcium and dietary fiber. Pearl barley has lower amounts of these nutrients and less dietary fiber.

Buckwheat

Technically buckwheat is not really a grain (a grass seed) but a fruit. It is so like a true grain that it is generally referred to as one. Buckwheat has a full, nutty flavor that is enhanced when the grain is toasted.

Uses: Buckwheat groats are delicious in pilafs and stuffings, with vegetables, rice or other grains, noodles or potatoes. Serve steamed buckwheat grits as a breakfast cereal. Use buckwheat flour in pancakes, Russian blini, breads and dumplings.

Nutritional Analysis: Buckwheat is rich in B Vitamins, Protein, Iron and Calcium.

Corn

Corn is the only grain that is eaten fresh as a vegetable. Cornmeal is finely ground from dried yellow or white corn.

Uses: Boiled cornmeal can be eaten as a breakfast cereal or molded, cooled, sliced and fried. Use cornmeal to make breads, muffins, puddings, pancakes and dumplings. Use it as a coating for fried foods. Coarsely ground cornmeal, called polenta, can be made into a mush and topped with butter, cheese, or a variety of sauces. Polenta mush can also be chilled, sliced, fried and topped with sauce. Serve with meat, fish or poultry.

Nutritional Analysis: Corn is not as good a source of vitamins and minerals as are some of the other grains, although it is the only grain that contains Vitamin A. It also contains significant amounts of B Vitamins, Calcium, Iron and Protein.

Millet

Bird feed and cattle feed are the primary uses of millet in the United States. Millet is a small, round, golden-yellow seed that does not need to be processed after harvesting so that only the hull is removed.

Uses: Millet works well with sweet, spicy, salty or sour flavors. It may be steamed and served as a breakfast cereal, made into a pilaf, baked in a pudding, added to stuffings and breads, used in a salad and eaten with most meats, fruits, and vegetables.

Nutritional Analysis: Millet is a good source of protein, B Vitamins, Potassium, Magnesium, Phosphorus, and Iron.

Oats

Oats are one of the few grains from which the bran and germ are not removed during processing. Oats are available in a variety of forms. OAT GROATS are whole oat grains that have been hulled. STEEL-CUT OATS are groats that have been sliced with steel blades. ROLLED OATS (old-fashioned oats) are groats that have been steamed and rolled flat. QUICK-COOKING ROLLED OATS are oat groats that have been steamed, rolled, and then cut into pieces which cook more quickly. INSTANT OATS are oats that have been partially cooked and dried before being rolled. OAT BRAN is the outer covering of the hulled oat.

Uses: Oats can be used as a breakfast cereal, in breads, cakes, cookies, granola, fruit crisps, pancakes, and muffins. Cooked whole oats can be added to soups or stews. Cooked oatmeal can be added to stuffings and meat loaves. It can also be molded, cooled, sliced and fried. Oat groats can be ground into flour.

Nutritional Analysis: All oat products contain some bran and are good sources of fiber. Oatmeal is an excellent source of protein. It is also a good source of B Vitamins, Vitamin E, Iron, Calcium, and Phosphorus.

Quinoa

Pronounced KEEN-wa, this grain is related to corn but it looks, cooks and tastes like a grain. Quinoa has more protein than any other grain and is well tolerated by those sensitive to wheat.

Uses: Quinoa cooks in just 15 minutes and is extremely light and fluffy. It is compatible with almost any food or seasoning as its flavor is quite mild. Substitute it for couscous, rice or other grains in side dishes, salads, casseroles and stuffings.

Rice

Rice is the staple grain for half the population of the world, and there are thousands of varieties available. LONG-GRAIN WHITE RICE is rice that has had its hull, bran, and germ removed, leaving the starchy endosperm. The grains are long and thin and usually opaque. It has a mild flavor and fluffy texture. LONG-GRAIN BROWN RICE is rice that has been hulled but still has its germ and bran intact. The long grains of this type of rice are beige in color and somewhat opaque. When cooked this rice has a fluffy texture and a grainy, nutty flavor. SHORT-GRAIN WHITE RICE comes in two varieties: The first is called either glutinous, sweet, sticky, mochi or pearl rice. It is very white and opaque and has a high starch content which makes it sticky when cooked. The second type of short-grain white rice is called arborio. It, too, has a high starch content and is used to make risotto as well as soups and rice puddings. SHORT-GRAIN BROWN RICE has a chewy, dense texture and a grainy, nutty flavor when cooked.

Uses: The various types of rice available can be used in countless ways. Use it as a side dish, salad, entrée, in soups, stews, pilafs, rice puddings, croquettes, with beans, in paella, jambalaya, arroz con pollo,

curries and stir-fries. Add it to pancakes, breads and muffins.

Nutritional Analysis:
Brown rice is a good source of dietary fiber, B Vitamins, Vitamin E, Iron, Phosphorus, Calcium and Potassium. White rice has less of these nutrients although enrichment returns some of the B Vitamins and Iron but not the dietary fiber or Vitamin E.

Rye

Rye has a strong, distinctive flavor. WHOLE-GRAIN RYE OR RYE BERRIES are rye berries whose outer hulls have been removed. RYE GRITS OR CRACKED RYE is whole rye that has been cracked into pieces. RYE FLAKES are rye berries that have been steamed and then flattened with steel rollers. RYE FLOUR is dark, medium or light depending on whether it's been made from the whole grain (dark), or from rye that has had the bran and/or germ removed (medium and light flours).

Uses: Whole-grain rye is delicious in soups, stuffings, stir-fry dishes and casseroles. Cracked rye can be used as a breakfast cereal or for pilafs. Rye flakes, like rolled oats, can be eaten as breakfast cereal, added to baked goods or meat loaves or used as a casserole topping. Rye flour has poor gluten-forming ability and makes a dense, chewy, strong-flavored loaf on its own. It is therefore best used in combination with wheat flour.

Nutritional Analysis: Rye is a good source of B Vitamins. It also contains Iron, Calcium, Phosphorus, Potassium, and fiber.

Triticale

Triticale is a hybrid of wheat and rye, designed to be as productive as wheat, as hardy as rye, and more nutritious than either. It is the first completely man-made grain.

Uses: Triticale has a mild, nutty flavor and thus works well with countless other foods. Use whole grain triticale berries in soups, stews, stuffings, pilafs and casseroles. Triticale flour, like rye flour, is low in gluten and so should be used in combination with other flours. Use it in making breads, muffins, cookies, pancakes and other baked goods.

Nutritional Analysis: Triticale is valued for its high protein content, higher than either wheat or rye.

Wheat

Wheat is the most widely grown and consumed grain in the world. There are at least 30,000 known varieties of wheat. An important distinction is between hard and soft varieties of wheat. Hard wheat has a high gluten forming ability and is thus used in making breads and pasta. Soft wheats have low gluten forming ability and are used for pastry flour to make cakes, cookies and pastries.

Varieties of wheat and their uses: WHOLE GRAIN WHEAT OR WHOLE WHEAT BERRIES are the whole kernel with just the hull removed. Use as you would rice, as a side dish, in salads, soups, stews, casseroles, pilafs, stuffings, breads and breakfast cereal. CRACKED WHEAT is wheat berries cut with steel blades into coarse, medium or fine pieces. Cooked cracked wheat has a nutty flavor and slightly crunchy texture. Use it as a breakfast cereal, in stuffings, pilafs, salads, and breads. BULGUR is whole wheat berries that have been steamed, dried and then cracked into varying degrees of coarseness. Use bulgur for salads, stuffings, breakfast cereals and pilafs. Add it to meat loaves, breads, and muffins. SEMOLINA is ground from the endosperm of durum wheat, a particularly hard wheat. Semolina has a very high gluten-forming ability. Because semolina dough is so firm and elastic, it is the flour used for most dried pastas. Use semolina as a breakfast cereal, in puddings and breads. COUSCOUS is made from semolina that has been steamed, rolled into tiny pellets and dried. Use couscous for the famous North African stews by the same name, eat it as a breakfast cereal, in pilafs, stuffings, casseroles and as a side dish with meat, fish or poultry. WHEAT GERM is most commonly found toasted and is valued for its nutty flavor and excellent nutritional content. Because of its high oil content, wheat germ turns rancid quickly unless stored in the refrigerator. Sprinkle wheat germ on cereal or yogurt, add it to breads, muffins, cookies, granola, and cooked cereals to boost the fiber and nutrition content. WHEAT BRAN is the outer coating of the wheat berry. Wheat bran is valued as a source of dietary fiber and is rarely used by itself.

Add it to cereals, meat loaves, breads, muffins, cookies and other baked goods for improved nutritive value. WHEAT FLAKES OR ROLLED WHEAT are steamed wheat berries that have been rolled flat. Use them as you would rolled oats. KAMUT and SPELT are two ancient species of wheat that are often better tolerated by those with wheat sensitivities. They do contain the protein gluten and hence are not suitable for gluten sensitive individuals (celiacs).

Nutritional Analysis: The less the wheat berry is processed, the higher its nutritional value. Whole-wheat berries, cracked wheat, wheat bran, and wheat germ are high in fiber. Bulgur, semolina and couscous have had the bran and germ removed and so have insignificant fiber content. Wheat germ is a good source of Vitamin E, protein and B Vitamins and dietary fiber. Wheat bran is the highest source of dietary fiber. It is also a good source of Magnesium, Phosphorus and B Vitamins. Without the bran and germ, wheat offers starch, some protein and B Vitamins.

Wild Rice

Wild rice is the seed of an aquatic grass, rather than a rice or a grain. Wild rice is dark brown and even longer than long-grain rice. It is never processed beyond removing the hull, so is eaten whole.

Uses: Wild rice has an earthy, nutty flavor and is delicious with earthy foods such as wild game, dark-meat fowl, mushrooms, and beans. It also goes well with meat, fish, poultry, fruits, vegetables and nuts. Combine it with white or brown rice for pilafs and salads. Add it to stuffings and soups. Wild rice can be ground into flour and used in combination with white flour to make breads, pancakes, waffles, crepes, muffins and other baked goods.

Nutritional Analysis: Wild rice is higher in protein and amino acids than true grains. It is also high in fiber, B Vitamins, Iron, Phosphorus, Magnesium, Calcium and Zinc.

BEANS

All beans are members of the legume family and are high in dietary fiber and nutrients such as Calcium, Iron and B Vitamins.

Preparing beans: Sort through packaged dried beans, removing any imperfect one. Beans bought in bulk may need more careful picking over before rinsing. After sorting, rinse beans well to remove dirt and dust. Most dried beans (except lentils and split peas) require soaking before cooking. Cover with cold water and soak eight hours or overnight. Or, for a quicker method: boil beans and water for two minutes; cover and let stand one hour. Soaking reduces cooking time about 15 minutes for quick-cooking beans and up to 30 minutes for slow-cooking ones.

Cooking beans: Cook in a proportion of three parts water to one part beans for the required amount of time. Simmer beans rather than cook them at a rapid boil.

Varieties of Beans and Uses:

ADZUKI is a small red bean with a soft texture and slightly sweet flavor when cooked. They are delicious eaten with rice. Adzuki beans are used to make red bean paste and a variety of sweet Asian dishes such as jellies, puddings and stuffed pastry.

BLACK BEANS, also called turtle beans, are a staple food in parts of Latin America and the Caribbean and are largely used in Japanese and Chinese cuisines as well. These small black beans have an earthy flavor and mealy texture. Use them in soups, stews, chilies, salads and bean dip. Combine them with rice, greens, pork, chicken and fish.

COWPEAS, one variety of which are BLACK-EYED PEAS, are very popular in the American South as well as in Africa. They have a mealy texture and an earthy flavor. These quick-cooking, easily-digested legumes  are a good natural source of selenium. Cowpeas go well with tomato, onion, and pork. Use them in soups, stews, and salads, or as a side dish. Hoppin' John is a popular southern dish of black eye peas.

CRANBERRY BEANS have mottled reddish markings. Use them in soups, especially Italian minestrone, stews, salads and as a side dish.

FAVA BEANS have a mealy texture and a strong, slightly bitter flavor. Add them to soups, stews, salads and serve them as a side dish.

FLAGEOLETS are small, light-green colored, kidney-shaped French beans. Braise flageolets and serve them with meats such as leg of lamb. Add them to soups, stews and salads.

GARBANZOS, also known as CHICK-PEAS or CECI BEANS, are popular in Indian, North African and Middle Eastern cuisines. These versatile, mildly nutty-flavored beans are delicious in salads, vegetable and grain dishes, soups, stews and as a side dish. Mashed and seasoned they make a wonderful spread or dip. They may be ground for flour to use for breads and fritters or roasted and served as a snack.

GREAT NORTHERN BEANS are large white shell beans. Use these mild flavored beans in soups, stews, salads and baked bean dishes.

KIDNEY BEANS come in both red and white varieties. The white are more commonly called CANNELLINI BEANS. These beans have a mealy texture and meaty flavor. They are delicious in chili, salads, soups and stews.

LENTILS are small flat

circular beans that cook in as little as 20 to 30 minutes. They can be found in yellow, pink, and greenish brown varieties. Lentils make delicious soups, stews, side dishes and salads. They are complemented by a wide range of flavors from onion and garlic to ginger and curry.

LIMA BEANS, also known as BUTTER BEANS, are large, kidney-shaped, light-green beans. They are great additions to soups, stews and salads as well as side dishes. They are commonly used to make succotash along with corn.

MUNG BEANS can be found in green, black and brown varieties. These highly digestible beans are known as moong dal or split golden gram in Indian cooking. They are valued as good sources of protein. Add them to soups, stews and grain dishes.

NAVY BEANS are small, white, oval beans that have long been a staple of the diet of the U.S. Navy; hence the name. Use navy beans to make baked beans, pork and beans, soups, stews and salads.

PIGEON PEAS are commonly found in the Caribbean, African and Indian cuisines. The dried peas are beige or pale yellow with red spots. In the Caribbean they are served with rice or made into dumplings or soup.

PINTO BEANS are popular mottled oval beans used especially in Mexican and southwestern cooking. They figure prominently in chilis, refried bean dishes, soups and stews.

SOYBEANS are small oval beans that come in yellow, green, brown, black and mottled varieties. They have a mild flavor and firm texture when cooked. Soybeans are valued for their high protein content and are used to make various products such as bean curd or tofu, soy milk, soy sauce, and soy flour. Dried soybeans can be sprouted and used in salads, sandwiches and stir-fries, or they can be boiled and added to soups, stews, salads or served as a side dish.

SPLIT PEAS may be green or yellow. Green split peas are easily digestible and have a wonderful flavor which make them extremely popular. They are usually used to make soups or purées. Yellow split peas have a different flavor than the green ones. Cook them with rice to make dal. They add body to broth and stocks, make soups heartier and are delicious added to green vegetable dishes.

Now your kitchen is fully equipped and you are ready to start cooking...

RESOURCES

Agriculture Handbook #8, Volumes 1-21 and Supplements, USDA. 1977-1992

Ancient Herbs in the J. Paul Getty Museum Jeanne D'Andrea The J. Paul Getty Museum, Malibu, CA, 1982

Bowes & Church's Food Values of Portions Commonly Used, 16th edition. Jean A.T. Perrington, editor. J.B Lippicett Co Philadelphia, 1995.

The Complete Idiot's Guide to Cooking Basics. Ronnie Fein, Alpha Books, Indianapolis, IN, 1995.

The Complete Whole Grain Cookbook. Carol Gelles, Donald I. Fine, Inc., New York, 1989.

Contemporary Nutrition Issues and Insights. Gordon M. Wardlaw, PhD, RD, LD, Paul M. Insel, PhD, Marcia F. Seyler, M. Phil., Mosby-Year Book, Inc., St. Louis, MO, 1994.

Cooking A to Z. Jane Horn, Editor, The Cole Group, Santa Rosa, California, 1992.

Eat Smart with Fresh Fruits and Vegetables. American Cancer Society, 1992

The Fannie Farmer Cookbook. Marion Cunningham, Alfred A. Knopf, New York, NY, 1990.

Fat and Cholesterol Counter. American Heart Association, Times Books, New York, NY, 1991

Foundations of Food Preparation. J.H. Freeland-Graves and G. C. Peckham, Macmillan Publishing Company, New York, NY, 1987, 5th Edition.

Herbalife Advanced Energy Guide. David B. Katzin, MD, PhD and Carolyn Katzin, MS, Herbalife International, Inc., Los Angeles, CA, 1994.

The Herbal Pantry. Emelie Tolley and Chris Mead, Clarkson Potter Publishers, New York, NY, 1992.

Nutritionist IV Software. The Hearst Corp. San Bruno, CA 1995

Produce, A Fruit and Vegetable Lovers' Guide. Bruce Beck, Friendly Press, Inc., New York, NY, 1984.

Recipes From an Ecological Kitchen. Lorna J. Sass, William Morrow and Co., Inc., New York, NY, 1992.

Chapter Four

Herbalife's Good Recipes

- Appetizers and Dips
- Beans
- Beverages and Shakes
- Breads, Cookies, Cakes and Pies
- Desserts, Fruits and Ices
- Fish and Shellfish
- Meat
- Pasta and Rice
- Poultry
- Salads and Relishes
- Sandwiches
- Sauces and Salad Dressings
- Soups and Broths
- Vegetables and Vegetarian Dishes

HERBALIFE'S GOOD RECIPES

The next section covers a wide range of recipes that reflect the Herbalife way of good eating. Most of the recipes provide less than 30% of their calories from fat but a few are higher. Overall, if you select foods from this cookbook, your daily caloric intake will average at about 20-25% fat even if you include some of the high-fat dressings and desserts. See pages 39 - 45 for seven day menu plans at 1200, 1500 and 2000 calories as examples. In every case we have reduced the fat from the original versions.

Each recipe reflects the Herbalife nutritional concepts and contains botanical factor rich foods. We choose olive oil to sauté or stir-fry and use butter only very sparingly when the recipe would not be the same without it. The emphasis is on vegetables and grains with lots of recipes to choose from. Enjoy!

NUTRITION INFORMATION

The nutrition information in the following section is based on USDA Food Table data which is derived from taking an average reading of a large number of samples of fruits and vegetables from various parts of the country at different times of the year. The nutritional content of individual recipes will vary according to the freshness of the produce used, the soil it was grown in and the season it was harvested. Refer to Chapter Three for selection of fresh produce.

Sodium information has been omitted because it varies with the amount you add to each recipe. The amount you add will depend on your personal taste and each recipe. Remember that most of the sodium in the diet comes from processed foods not from those you prepare yourself at home. We do not recommend exceeding one teaspoon of salt per person per day (2,400 milligrams).

Appetizers and Dips

Babaghanoush

2	medium eggplants
1	tablespoon lemon juice
1	tablespoon tahini
2	tablespoons fresh parsley, chopped
1	pinch cumin powder (optional)
1 1/2	tablespoons nonfat yogurt
1	clove garlic, crushed

Serves 4
Prep Time: 0:25

Total Calories 90
Protein 4g
Carbohydrate 16g
Fat 2g
Cholesterol 0gm
Dietary Fiber 3g
% Calories from
Fat 22%

Bake the eggplant in a medium oven until cooked through (about 20 minutes). Remove the skin and place in a blender. Add the tahini, yogurt, garlic, lemon juice and cumin powder. Blend to desired consistency. Season to taste and chill before serving. Garnish with chopped parsley.

Notes: Good source of Folacin

Baby Shrimp Cocktail

8	ounces shrimp, peeled
2	tablespoons light mayonnaise
1	tablespoon ketchup
3	drops Tabasco sauce
1	head limestone or butter lettuce
4	wedges lemon

Serves: 4
Prep Time: 0.10

Total Calories 11
Protein 2g
Carbohydrate 2g
Fat 2g
Cholesterol 89mg
Dietary Fiber 0g
% Calories from
Fat 12%

Combine the mayonnaise, ketchup and Tabasco sauce together in a bowl. Add the baby shrimp and mix well. Lay the lettuce leaves in the base of individual appetizer dishes and arrange the shrimp mixture on the top. Garnish with the lemon wedges and fresh parsley. Serve chilled.

Notes: Excellent source of Vitamin C. Good source of Niacin, Calcium and Iron.

Bean Dip

1/2	cup beans, soaked overnight
1/2	tablespoon extra virgin olive oil
2	tablespoons salsa
1	tablespoon fresh chives, chopped
1/4	teaspoon salt
1/4	teaspoon black pepper, fresh ground

Serves: 5
Prep Time: 0:30

Total Calories: 106
Protein 6g;
Carbohydrate 16g
Fat 2g
Cholesterol 0mg
Dietary Fiber 6g
% Calories from
Fat 19%

Rinse and drain the beans (any type is good). Boil for 20 minutes or until tender. If using canned beans, drain. Transfer to a blender and blend until smooth. Add the salsa, oil, salt and black pepper and continue to blend. Place in a serving bowl and chill. Serve with blue corn chips as an appetizer.

Notes: Excellent source of Folacin. Good source of Vitamin B1. You can use the recipe for Salsa or bottled salsa. Canned beans may also be used.

Bruschetta

4	slices Italian bread
2	garlic cloves
1/2	tablespoon olive oil
4	plum tomatoes, sliced
2	tablespoons fresh basil, chopped
1/2	teaspoon black pepper, fresh ground

Use a broiler to toast the bread on both sides. Rub the upper surfaces with garlic and sprinkle with olive oil. Top with slices of tomato and sprinkle with fresh basil and black pepper. Serve immediately while the toast is still warm.

Notes: Excellent source of Vitamin C. Good source of Vitamin A, B1, B2, Folacin and Niacin.

Serves: 4
Prep Time: 0:15

Total Calories 123
Protein 4g;
Carbohydrate 21g
Fat 3g
Cholesterol 0mg
Dietary Fiber 2g
% Calories from
Fat 22%

Ceviche

1	pound halibut
1/2	cup fresh lemon juice
2	medium tomatoes
1	small green bell pepper
2	tablespoons extra virgin olive oil
4	tablespoons fresh parsley
1	tablespoon white wine vinegar
dash	Tabasco sauce
1/2	teaspoon oregano
1/2	teaspoon salt
1/4	teaspoon pepper

Serves: 4
Prep Time:
0:10
Marinating time:
2:00+

Total Calories 170
Protein 25g
Carbohydrate 8g
Fat 4g
Cholesterol 36mg
Dietary Fiber 1g
% Calories from
Fat 24%

Dice the fish. Place in a glass bowl and cover with lemon juice. Refrigerate the marinated fish for at least 2 hours, turning the fish occasionally. Peel, remove the seeds and dice the tomatoes and add to the fish. Remove the seeds from the green bell pepper and dice. Add to the fish with the olive oil, parsley, vinegar, Tabasco, oregano, salt and pepper. Serve chilled garnished with olives and sprigs of parsley.

Notes: Excellent source of Vitamin C, A, B6, B12, Niacin and Iron. Good source of Vitamin B1 and Folacin.

Chicken Liver Paté

3/4	pound chicken livers
1/2	medium Spanish onion
1	stalk celery, finely chopped
1/4	small green bell pepper, finely chopped
2	egg whites, hard boiled
1/4	teaspoon salt
1/2	teaspoon black pepper, fresh ground
1	teaspoon olive oil

Serves: 6
Prep Time: 0:05
Stand Time: 0:30

Total Calories 90
Protein 12 g
Carbohydrate 4 g
Fat 3g
Cholesterol 249 mg
Dietary Fiber 0g.
% Calories from
Fat 30%

In a non stick skillet sprayed with olive oil, gently saute the chicken livers for 2-3 minutes until firm but not completely cooked through. Place the livers and hard boiled egg whites together in a blender and blend until smooth. Add the celery and green bell pepper and combine by hand with the seasonings. Place in a paté dish or small soufflé dish and chill in the refrigerator. A thin layer of clarified butter on top will keep the paté fresh for a few days in the refrigerator. Serve garnished with a little chopped parsley and with triangles of thinly sliced toast.

Notes: Excellent source of Vitamin C, A, B6, B12, B2, Folacin, Niacin and Iron. Good source of Zinc.

If you like paté, this is a lower fat, lower cholesterol version that still retains good flavor. Liver paté is a nutritious appetizer.

Crab Dip

1	pound crab meat, drained or surimi-based "krab"
1	cup sour cream, light or fat free
dash	Tabasco sauce
1/2	teaspoon black pepper, fresh ground
1	teaspoon red wine vinegar
1/2	teaspoon extra virgin olive oil

Mix the ingredients together in a large bowl. Refrigerate overnight and serve with crackers, raw vegetables or pumpernickel bread.

Notes: Excellent source of Vitamin B12, Folacin and Zinc.

Serves: 4
Prep Time: 0:05
Stand Time: 1:00+

Total Calories 143
Protein 25g;
Carbohydrate 1g
Fat 4g
Cholesterol 106mg
Dietary Fiber 1g
Fat 24%

Curry Dip

1/3	cup plain low fat yogurt
2	teaspoons curry powder
1	teaspoon fresh lemon juice
2	drops Tabasco sauce
1/4	teaspoon black pepper, fresh ground
1	teaspoon sugar

Combine the ingredients together and place in a serving dish. Garnish with cayenne or paprika. Serve with crackers and fresh vegetables.

Notes: Good source of Vitamin C.

Serves: 4
Prep Time: 0:05

Total Calories 20
Protein 1g
Carbohydrate 3g
Fat 2g
Cholesterol 1mg
Dietary Fiber 0g
% Calories from
Fat 18%

Dolmathes

2	tablespoons olive oil
3	tablespoons water
2	large onions
1	cup white rice
2	tablespoons fresh mint, chopped
1/2	cup raisins
1	tablespoon pine nuts
1/2	lemon, juiced
35	medium grape leaves, canned

Serves: 6
Prep Time: 0:50
Stand Time: 1:00+

Total Calories 209
Protein 4g
Carbohydrate 38g
Fat 6g
Cholesterol 0mg
Dietary Fiber 2g
% Calories from
Fat 24%

In a skillet simmer the onion, water and oil until transparent. Add the rice and mint and season with salt and pepper. Cook over a low heat for 5 minutes adding a little more water if necessary. Cool and add the raisins, pine nuts and lemon juice. Line the bottom of a 3 quart saucepan with two large grape leaves and lay a medium leaf with the stem towards your wrist in an open palm. Place a spoonful of the rice mixture in the middle and bring the sides around and roll towards your fingers. Place the roll in the saucepan on top of the large leaves. Continue until all the rice mixture is gone. Cover with two more large leaves and add a saucer or small plate with a weight on top. Add water so a little shows around the edges of the rolls. Bring to the boil and simmer over a low heat until the water is absorbed (about 45 minutes). Remove and cool in the refrigerator. Serve at room temperature with lemon wedges and garnished with cilantro or parsley.

Notes: Excellent source of Vitamin B1 and Folacin. Good source of Vitamin C and Iron.

French Beans and Bay Shrimp

1	pound French beans
1/2	pound bay shrimp, cooked
2	tablespoons olive oil
1	tablespoon white wine vinegar
1	clove garlic, crushed
1/4	teaspoon black pepper, fresh ground
1	tablespoon shallots, finely chopped

Serves: 8
Prep Time: 0:20

Total Calories 254
Protein 17 g
Carbohydrate 37 g
Fat 5 g
Cholesterol 55 mg
Dietary Fiber 3g
% Calories from
Fat 18%

Steam or microwave the French beans until cooked but crunchy. Combine the olive oil, white wine vinegar, garlic, shallots and black pepper together in a mixing bowl. Arrange the drained French beans on a serving dish with the shrimp on top. Cover with the dressing and chill for 5 minutes prior to serving. Garnish with sprigs of parsley and lemon wedges.

Notes: Excellent source of Vitamin, B1, and Folacin. Good
source of Vitamin B6, B2, Niacin, Calcium and Iron.

Gravlax

1	pound Atlantic salmon, filleted
1	tablespoon juniper berries
1	tablespoon black peppercorns
2	tablespoons salt
1	tablespoon sugar
1	tablespoon fresh lemon juice
2	tablespoons fresh dill, chopped
2	shallots, chopped

Serves: 6
Prep Time:
0:10
Marinating time:
36:00
Stand Time: 24:00+

Total Calories 126
Protein 16g
Carbohydrate 5g
Fat 3g
Cholesterol 39mg
Dietary Fiber 0g
% Calories from
Fat 23%

Place the salmon fillet in a glass dish. Make the marinade by crushing the peppercorns with the juniper berries and combining salt, pepper, sugar, lemon juice, chopped dill and shallots. Add the marinade to the salmon. Cover the dish and refrigerator for 36 hours turning three times. Make sure the dish is tightly sealed. Slice the salmon into thin sheets and serve at room temperature garnished with fresh dill weed. Serve with a mustard and dill sauce .

Notes: Excellent source of Vitamin A, B12 and Niacin. Good source of Vitamin B6 and B1.

Guacamole

2	avocados
1/4	cup fresh lemon juice
1	clove garlic, crushed
6	tomatoes, peeled and chopped
1	medium onion, chopped
1	green bell pepper, peeled and chopped
1	tablespoon fresh cilantro leaf, finely chopped
1/2	teaspoon salt
1/4	teaspoon black pepper, fresh ground

Serves: 4
Prep Time: 0:10

Total Calories 214
Protein 4g
Carbohydrate 19g
Fat 16g
Cholesterol 0mg
Dietary Fiber 5g
% Calories from
Fat 60%

Peel, remove the pit and mash the avocado. Add the lemon juice, garlic, tomatoes, onion and pepper. Stir in the cilantro. Replace the avocado pit to keep the guacamole from turning brown. Serve with corn chips.

Notes: Excellent source of Vitamin C, A, B6, Folacin. Good source of Vitamin B1, B2, Niacin and Iron.
Eat sparingly as this is a high-fat food. Fat content is of good fatty acid profile and this dish is a good source of antioxidants.

Mushrooms a la Grecque

1 1/2	pound button mushrooms
3	tomatoes
1	tablespoon olive oil
1	tablespoon water
3	tablespoons white wine vinegar
6	coriander seed
1	bay leaf
1	teaspoon thyme
1	clove garlic, crushed

Serves: 4
Prep Time: 0:15
Stand Time: 0:30+

Total Calories 120
Protein 4g
Carbohydrate 15g
Fat 6g
Cholesterol 0mg
Dietary Fiber 3g
% Calories from
Fat 36%

Remove the skins from the tomatoes by making a tiny incision on the surface and covering the tomatoes with boiling water. Leave for one minute then drain water and peel away the skins. Halve the tomatoes, remove the seeds and chop the flesh coarsely. Place the oil, wine, water, coriander seeds, bay leaf, thyme, garlic and seasonings in a pan. Bring to the boil and simmer gently for 5 minutes. Add the mushrooms and tomato flesh, cover the pan and continue cooking for 5 minutes. Remove the vegetables and place on a serving dish. Reduce the wine and oil mixture by boiling for 5 minutes. Pour the thickened mixture over the mushrooms and leave to cool. Serve cold as an appetizer or as a side salad.

Notes: Excellent source of Vitamin C, B2, Folacin, Niacin and Iron. Good source of Vitamin A, B6, B1 and Zinc.

Steamed Mussels in White Wine

4	dozen mussels
4	shallots, finely chopped
1	cup white wine
2	sprigs fresh thyme
1	bay leaf
1/2	teaspoon black pepper, fresh ground
1/2	tablespoon extra virgin olive oil
1	tablespoon fresh parsley, chopped

Serves: 4
Prep Time: 0:20

Total Calories 215
Protein 19g
Carbohydrate 12g
Fat 5g
Cholesterol 42mg
Dietary Fiber 0g
% Calories from
Fat 21%

Wash, scrape and debeard the mussels under running water. Discard any with cracked, broken or open shells. Heat the oil in a large non-stick pan and sauté the shallots for 2-3 minutes. Add the wine, parsley, thyme and bay leaf. Season with the pepper and simmer gently for 10 minutes. Add the mussels, cover the pan and allow them to steam. Shake constantly so all of them are evenly exposed and their shells will open. Toss the ones that stay closed. Remove the mussels and arrange in a serving dish. Remove the bay leaf. Reduce the cooking liquid a little and pour over the mussels. Serve garnished with fresh ground parsley.

Notes: Excellent source of Vitamin C, A, B6, B12, B2, B1
Folacin, Iron and Zinc. Good source of Vitamin B6,
Niacin and Calcium.

Tiny Meatballs

I	cup rice, cooked
3/4	pound lamb shank, ground
I	medium onion, chopped
I/2	cup fresh parsley, chopped fine
I	teaspoon extra virgin olive oil
2	egg whites
I	teaspoon fresh thyme, chopped fine
I/2	teaspoon black pepper, fresh ground
I/4	teaspoon salt
I/2	cup flour, all-purpose

Serves: 6
Prep Time: 0:20

Total Calories 260
Protein 12g
Carbohydrate 34g
Fat 7g
Cholesterol 30mg
Dietary Fiber 1g
% Calories from
Fat 25%

Lightly beat the egg whites with a fork and add the olive oil, rice, onion, parsley and thyme. Add the ground lamb, season with salt and pepper and combine well. Form 1" round or oval shapes on a floured surface and roll in flour. Heat a heavy non stick skillet and quickly brown the meatballs (2-3 minutes). Lay them in an ovenproof dish and place in a low temperature oven (200°F) for 15 minutes. Serve warm with cocktail sticks and garnished with fresh parsley.

Notes: Excellent source of Vitamin B12, B1, Niacin and Iron
Good source of Vitamin B2 and Zinc. Larger size
meatballs will need to be cooked through in a low
temperature oven (200 °F) for 20 minutes. These can be
served with a tomato sauce as a main dish .

Zucchini Strips

4	medium zucchini
1	medium onion, chopped
2	tablespoons Parmesan cheese, grated
1/2	cup bread crumbs
2	tablespoons fresh parsley, chopped
1/2	teaspoon salt
1/2	teaspoon black pepper, fresh ground
1/2	teaspoon marjoram
1	teaspoon olive oil
1	tablespoon liquid egg substitute

Serves: 8
Prep Time: 0:30

Total Calories 54
Protein 3g
Carbohydrate 8g
Fat 2g
Cholesterol 1mg
Dietary Fiber 1g
% Calories form
Fat 25%

Slice the zucchini into 2" strips and slice in half. Scoop out the middle and arrange on a heat proof dish. Combine the egg substitute, olive oil, cheese, parsley, marjoram and seasonings together and fill the zucchini slices. Bake in the oven for 15 minutes until brown. Serve hot.

Beans

Adzuki Beans and Rice

Serves: 4
Prep Time: 2:00 (20)

Total Calories 390
Protein 14g
Carbohydrate 73g
Fat 4g
Cholesterol 0mg
Dietary Fiber 8g
% Calories from
Fat 10%

1	cup adzuki beans
1	medium onion
2	cloves garlic
1	teaspoon salt
1	tablespoon olive oil
1	cup rice
1/2	cup vegetable broth
1/4	teaspoon chili powder

Wash beans and cover with water. Bring to a boil, remove from heat and let soak for one hour. Drain and add sufficient cold water to cover the beans. Add chopped onion, crushed garlic cloves and salt. Canned beans may be used. Bring to the boil and simmer for 1 1/2 hours until tender. Add extra water if necessary. Place bean mixture in a blender and purée till smooth. Cook rice using broth as the liquid. Add chili powder to cooked rice and set aside. Heat olive oil in a heavy skillet and add puréed bean mixture. Simmer for 5 minutes, stirring frequently. Stir in rice and heat for a further 5 minutes. Serve with a fresh salad.

Notes: Excellent source of Vitamin B1, Folacin, Niacin, Iron
and Zinc. Good source of Vitamin A and B6.

Baked Beans

3	cups pinto beans, canned
1	large onion
1	15 ounce can tomato sauce
1/2	teaspoon mustard powder
1	teaspoon chili powder
1	teaspoon honey or molasses

Preheat oven to 350°F. Chop onions and add to beans, tomatoes, onions, honey and seasonings. Bake in an oiled, uncovered casserole dish for an hour. This may be kept warm in a covered pot. Serve with hot bread and a mixed salad. Optional: Add one cup chopped apple (with peel on).

Notes: Excellent source of Folacin. Good source of Vitamin C, A, B6, B1, B2, Iron and Zinc.

Serves: 4
Prep Time: 1:00

Total Calories 174
Protein 10
Carbohydrate 34g
Fat 2g
Cholesterol 0mg
Dietary Fiber 8g
% Calories from
Fat 1%

Bean, Noodle and Nut Casserole

12	ounces noodles
1	pound blackeyed peas
1/2	tablespoon olive oil
4	medium onions
4	ounces cashews
4	ounces peanuts

Serves: 10
Prep Time: 2:30 (20)
Reduce the prep
time by 2 hours
using canned beans.

Total Calories 429
Protein 21g
Carbohydrate 59g
Fat 14g
Cholesterol 0mg
Dietary Fiber 8g
% Calories from
Fat 28%

Wash blackeyed peas. Boil 4 cups of water and drop the blackeyed peas in. Boil for 2 minutes. Set aside to soak for one hour. Cook noodles according to package instructions. Melt butter and sauté onions until clear and soft. Toss nuts with onions in the frying pan until browned lightly. Drain blackeyed peas and cover with 4 cups of cold water. Bring back to a boil and simmer for 30 minutes or until tender. Combine drained noodles, blackeyed peas, onions and nuts in a casserole dish. Cover and heat for 20 minutes in a 350° oven. Serve with tomato sauce and a fresh salad.

Notes: Excellent source of Vitamin B6, B12, B1, B2, Folacin, Niacin, Iron and Zinc. Good source of Calcium. This is a satisfying vegetarian entree.

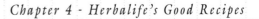

Blackeyed Peas

2	quarts water
1	pound blackeyed peas
1	medium onion
1	teaspoon salt
1	red pepper pod, crushed
1	pound ground turkey
2	cloves garlic, crushed
1	teaspoon garlic powder
1	pinch baking soda

Bring water to boil. Add washed blackeyed peas, onion, garlic, salt, garlic powder and crushed red pepper pod. Cook on low heat until the peas are tender (about one hour). Mash the peas with a large wooden spoon then add ground turkey, ginger and baking soda. Adjust water to give a mushy consistency.

Notes: Excellent source of Vitamin B6, B1, Folacin, Niacin, Iron and Zinc. Good source of Vitamin C, B2 and Calcium.

Serves: 6
Prep Time: 1:30 (15)
Reduce the prep time by 1 hour by using canned peas

Total Calories 376
Protein 31g
Carbohydrate 48g
Fat 7g
Cholesterol 60mg
Dietary Fiber 8g
% Calories from Fat 17%

Colorful Bean Salad

1/2	cup onion chopped
1/2	cup green pepper, chopped
1/4	cup olive oil
1/2	cup vinegar
1	tablespoon sugar
1/3	teaspoon pepper
1	small jar pimiento, chopped
1	can yellow beans
1	can kidney beans
1	can green beans

Serves: 4
Prep Time: 0:05

Total Calories 474
Protein 22g
Carbohydrate 66g
Fat 15g
Cholesterol 0mg
Dietary Fiber 13g
% Calories from
Fat 28%

Drain the beans. Mix the olive oil, vinegar and sugar in the bottom of the serving dish. Add the other ingredients. Garnish with chopped cilantro. Serve chilled.

Notes: Excellent source of Vitamin C, B6, B1, Folacin, Niacin, Iron and Zinc. Good source of Vitamin B2 and Calcium.

Flageolets (Small French Green Beans)

2	cups flageolets, soaked
4	cups water
I	tablespoon olive oil
I	medium onion, chopped
2	cloves garlic, crushed
1/2	teaspoon salt
1/2	teaspoon black pepper
I	tablespoon parsley, chopped

Serves: 6
Prep Time: 1:30
Reduce prep time to
10 minutes by using
canned beans.

Total Calories 228
Protein 13g
Carbohydrate 42g
Fat 3g
Cholesterol 0mg
Dietary Fiber 12g
% Calories from
Fat 10%

Soak flageolets overnight. Drain and rinse. Heat the water in a pot. Heat the olive oil in a large skillet. Sauté the onion and garlic until lightly browned and soft (about 5 minutes). Stir in the drained flageolets and heat for 3 minutes over a low flame. Add the hot water and cover the pan. Simmer for one hour. Add extra water if necessary. Adjust seasoning and serve sprinkled with fresh, chopped parsley.

Notes: Excellent source of Vitamin B1, Folacin, Iron and Zinc.
Good source of Vitamin B6 and Calcium.
Reduce preparation time by using canned beans.

Lentil and Pecan Casserole

2	cups lentils
1	tablespoon olive oil
1/4	teaspoon thyme
1/2	cup pecans
1	teaspoon soy sauce
1	tablespoon cheddar cheese, low-fat, shredded

Serves: 4
Prep Time: 2:00
Reduce prep time to 10 minutes by using canned lentils.

Total Calories 435
Protein 29g
Carbohydrate 58g
Fat 12g
Cholesterol 0mg
Dietary Fiber 30g
% Calories from Fat 24%

Soak beans overnight in cold water. Drain and bring to the boil. Simmer until tender. Preheat the oven to 350°F. Crush the beans. Add chopped pecans and seasonings. Place in an oiled skillet. Heat for 15 minutes. Add grated cheese and continue heating until melted (3-5 minutes). Serve with a green salad.

Notes: Excellent source of Vitamin B6, B1, Folacin, Iron and Zinc. Good source of Vitamin C, B2 and Niacin.

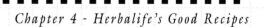

Lentil Patties

1	cup lentils, canned
1	medium onion
1	tablespoon olive oil
1	clove garlic
1/2	teaspoon salt
1/4	teaspoon ground cumin
1/2	teaspoon curry powder
1	pinch celery salt
3/4	cup bread crumbs
1	tablespoon liquid egg substitute or 1 egg

Serves: 4
Prep Time: 0:30

Total Calories 303
Protein 18g
Carbohydrate 44g
Fat 3g
Cholesterol 53mg
Dietary Fiber 16g
% Calories from
Fat 9%

Preheat oven to 350°F. Stir lentils and seasonings together in a bowl. Add half of the bread crumbs. Lightly beat the egg with a fork and add to the mixture to bind (this step is optional). Using wet hands, mold the lentil mixture into 8 evenly shaped patties. Place the remaining bread crumbs into a large plastic bag. Add the patties and roll them in the crumbs inside the bag until evenly covered. Remove the patties and set aside. Heat the olive oil in a skillet and lightly fry the patties to brown them. Place the skillet in the oven and bake for 20 minutes. Serve with a tomato or yogurt based sauce.

Notes: Excellent source of Vitamin B6, B1, Folacin and Iron.
Good source of Vitamin B2, Niacin and Zinc.

Lima Beans with Ham and Sage

1	16 oz package frozen baby lima beans
1/2	tablespoon olive oil
1	medium onion, chopped
2	stalks celery, chopped
1	clove garlic, minced
1	ounce ham, julienned
1	tablespoon fresh parsley, chopped
1	teaspoon fresh sage, chopped
1/4	teaspoon salt
1/4	teaspoon black pepper
1	teaspoon white wine vinegar

Serves: 4
Prep Time: 0:15

Total Calories 95
Protein 5g
Carbohydrate 13g
Fat 3g
Cholesterol 4mg
Dietary Fiber 3g
% Calories from
Fat 25%

Boil the lima beans as directed on the package. Heat the oil in a non stick skillet. Sauté the onions and garlic for 3-5 minutes. Add the celery and sauté for another minute. Add the lima beans, ham, parsley and sage and cook for 2 minutes. Serve hot with rice as a main dish.

Notes: Good source of Vitamin C, B6, B1 and Folacin.

Mexican Bean Pie

4	corn tortillas
1/2	cup scallions, sliced thin
2	cloves garlic, crushed
2	green bell peppers, diced
1	tablespoon olive oil
2	cups pinto beans, cooked, mashed
2	tomatoes, chopped
2	teaspoons chili powder
1	teaspoon coriander ground
1/2	cup egg substitute, liquid
1/4	cup cheddar cheese, low-fat, shredded

Serves: 4
Prep Time: 0:45

Total Calories 281
Protein 15g
Carbohydrate 41g
Fat 6g
Cholesterol 2mg
Dietary Fiber 11g
% Calories form
Fat 21%

Heat tortillas for 5-8 minutes over a flame or in a hot oven. Place in a blender or pestle and mortar and crumble finely. Take 4 pie pans (5" in diameter) and spray or coat with olive oil. Coat with the tortilla crumbs, setting aside extra for topping. Heat the rest of the olive oil in a heavy skillet and sauté the scallions, peppers and garlic for about 3-4 minutes, until tender. Add the beans, tomatoes, chili powder and coriander and continue to sauté for a further 5 minutes. Remove from the heat and stir in the egg substitute. Divide among the prepared pans and sprinkle the tops with the rest of the crumbs. Bake at 375°F for 20 minutes. Top with cheese and melt for a further few minutes in the hot oven. Serve with a salad.

Notes: Excellent source of Vitamin C, A, B6, B1, Folacin and Iron. Good source of Vitamin B2, Calcium and Zinc.

Navy Bean Stew

1/2	pound navy beans
2	tablespoons olive oil
1	large onion
1	clove garlic
1/2	cup tomato sauce
1	medium carrot
1	stalk celery
1/4	teaspoon black pepper
1/4	cup parsley sprigs
1	teaspoon dried basil
4	cups water

Serves: 4
Prep Time: 0:15 (30)

Total Calories 279
Protein 14g
Carbohydrate 41g
Fat 8g
Cholesterol 0mg
Dietary Fiber 16g
% Calories from
Fat 24%

Soak rinsed and sorted navy beans in water overnight or use the short method by covering with 2 1/2 cups of cold water, bringing to a boil for 2 minutes and then letting stand for one hour. Drain. Canned beans may be used.

Heat olive oil in large soup pot and sauté chopped onions and crushed garlic clove until lightly browned and moist. Add tomato sauce, thinly sliced carrot, chopped celery, black pepper and simmer for 10 more minutes. Add navy beans and 4 cups of boiling water. Lower the heat and simmer in the covered pot until the beans are tender (about 45 minutes). Serve with hot bread or pasta salad for a nourishing main dish.

Notes: Excellent source of Vitamin C, A, B6, B2, B1, Folacin and Iron. Good source of Vitamin B2, Niacin, Calcium and Zinc.

Southern Style Beans and Rice

1	cup canned red kidney beans
1	medium onion, chopped
1	small green bell pepper
1	pinch salt
1/4	teaspoon black pepper
1/2	teaspoon Cajun seasoning
1	cup rice

Serves: 6
Prep Time: 0:20

Total Calories 224
Protein 10g
Carbohydrate 46g
Fat 1g
Cholesterol 0mg
Dietary Fiber 6g
% Calories from
Fat 2%

Drain and rinse the beans. Meanwhile cook the rice by covering with 1/2 " water and simmer in a covered pan until the water has been absorbed and the rice is cooked. Sauté the onion, garlic and chopped pepper for 6-8 minutes until browned and cooked. Add the beans and sufficient water to make a thick gravy. Season with the Cajun seasoning, salt and freshly ground black pepper. Serve with the rice.

Notes: Excellent source of Vitamin C, B1 and Folacin. Good source of Vitamin B6, Niacin, Iron and Zinc.

Spicy Bean Chili

3/4	pound extra lean ground beef
2	large onions
2	cloves garlic
4	cups red kidney beans, cooked
1	can tomatoes, stewed
2	tablespoons chili powder
1	teaspoon ground cumin
1/2	teaspoon oregano
1	teaspoon thyme
1	small can corn kernels

Serves: 6
Prep Time: 0:40

Total Calories 326
Protein 23g
Carbohydrate 37g
Fat 9g
Cholesterol 39mg
Dietary Fiber 11g
% Calories from
Fat 25%

Heat oil and saute chopped onions and crushed garlic in a large, non-stick pan. Remove the onions and garlic and set aside. Add the ground beef to the pan and heat for 5 minutes, crushing it with a wooden spoon. Drain excess oil and return the onions and garlic to the pan. Add the beans, tomatoes and seasonings and bring to a boil. Reduce the heat and simmer until the consistency is thick and creamy (about 20-30 minutes). Add corn and heat again for a few minutes. More chili powder or crushed red chili peppers may be added to taste.

Notes: Excellent source of Vitamin A, C, B6, B12, B1, Folacin, Niacin, Iron and Zinc. Good source of Vitamin B2.

Beverages

and Shakes

Aloha Delight

1	cup skim milk
2	tablespoons Formula 1 French Vanilla
1/2	teaspoon coconut extract
1/2	teaspoon pineapple extract
1	tablespoon orange juice
3	ice cubes

Combine ingredients in a blender and blend until smooth.
Serve chilled, garnished with fresh pineapple and a sprig of
mint.

Notes: Excellent source of Vitamin C, B1, B2, Calcium and
Iron. Good source of Vitamin A and B6.

Serves: 1
Prep Time: 0:05

Total Calories 186
Protein 17g
Carbohydrate 24g
Fat 1g
Cholesterol 4mg
Dietary Fiber 3g
% Calories from
Fat 6%

Apple Pie Shake

2	tablespoons Formula 1 French Vanilla
1/4	cup apples
dash	nutmeg
1/2	teaspoon cinnamon
1	cup skim milk
3	ice cubes

Blend all ingredients together and serve chilled.

Notes: Excellent source of Vitamin C, B6, B12, B1, B2, Folacin,
Calcium, Iron and Zinc. Good source of Vitamin A.

Serves: 1
Prep Time: 0:10

Total Calories 184
Protein 16g
Carbohydrate 27g
Fat 1g
Cholesterol 4mg
Dietary Fiber 4g
% Calories from
Fat 6%

Banana Fruit Shake

2	tablespoons Formula 1 French Vanilla
4	ounces nonfat yogurt
4	fluid ounces water
1/2	cup frozen peach slices
1/2	medium banana
3	ice cubes

Blend all ingredients and serve chilled, garnished with a slice of banana.

Notes: Excellent source of Vitamin C, B6, B1, B2, Iron and Zinc. Good source of Calcium.

Serves: 1
Prep Time: 0:05

Total Calories 310
Protein 16g
Carbohydrate 62g
Fat 1g
Cholesterol 2mg
Dietary Fiber 6g
% Calories from Fat 3%

Black Forest Shake

2	tablespoons Formula 1 Dutch Chocolate
1/2	teaspoon black walnut extract
8	fluid ounces skim milk
1/2	banana
4	ice cubes

Combine ingredients in a blender and serve chilled garnished with chocolate sprinkles.

Notes: Excellent source of Vitamin C, B6, B12, B1, B2, Calcium and Zinc. Good source of Vitamin A and Iron.

Serves: 1
Prep Time: 0:05

Total Calories 175
Protein 16g
Carbohydrate 26g
Fat 1g
Cholesterol 9mg
Dietary Fiber 16g
% Calories from Fat 5%

Cappuccino Shake

2	tablespoons Formula 1 Dutch Chocolate
4	fluid ounces skim milk
3	ice cubes
4	ounces non-fat vanilla frozen yogurt
1	tablespoon instant coffee

Serves: 1
Prep Time: 0:05

Total Calories 196
Protein 19g
Carbohydrate 28g
Fat 1g
Cholesterol 4mg
Dietary Fiber 0g
% Calories from
Fat 4%

Place all ingredients in a blender and mix until smooth.

Notes: Excellent source of Vitamin B12, B2 and Calcium.

Coffee Shake

2	tablespoons Formula 1 French Vanilla
1	teaspoon instant coffee
8	fluid ounces skim milk
1/2	peach
3	ice cubes

Serves: 1
Prep Time: 0:05

Total Calories 165
Protein 16g
Carbohydrate 22g
Fat 1g
Cholesterol 4mg
Dietary Fiber 3g
% Calories from
Fat 6%

Combine ingredients in a blender and serve chilled, garnished with a slice of peach.

Notes: Excellent source of Vitamin C, B6, B12, B1, B2, Calcium, Iron and Zinc. Good source of Vitamin A.

Extra Chocolatey Shake

1	cup skim milk
1/4	teaspoon vanilla extract
1/4	teaspoon chocolate syrup
1	teaspoon Hershey's cocoa
2	tablespoons Formula 1 Dutch Chocolate
3	ice cubes

Combine all the ingredients in a blender and blend until smooth. Serve chilled, garnished with chocolate sprinkles.

Notes: Excellent source of Vitamin B12, B2 and Calcium. Good source of Vitamin A. Optional addition: 1 teaspoon instant coffee.

Serves: 1
Prep Time: 0:05

Total Calories 184
Protein 17g
Carbohydrate 28g
Fat 1g
Cholesterol 9mg
Dietary Fiber 49g
% Calories from
Fat 5%

Fruit-Juicy Shake

2	tablespoons Formula 1 Wild Berry
8	fluid ounces cranberry juice, low calorie
4	strawberries
3	cubes ice

Combine ingredients in a blender and serve chilled, garnished with a strawberry.

Notes: Excellent source of Vitamin C, B6, B1, B2, Iron and Zinc. Good source of Calcium.

Serves: 1
Prep Time: 0:05

Total Calories 125
Protein 8g
Carbohydrate 21g
Fat 1g
Cholesterol 0mg
Dietary Fiber 3g
% Calories from
Fat 7%

Serves: 8
Prep Time: 0:20

Total Calories 122
Protein <1g
Carbohydrate 17g
Fat 1g
Cholesterol 0mg
Dietary Fiber 1g
% Calories from
Fat 3%

Gluhwein

1/2	cup water
1	lemon
24	fluid ounces red wine
1	pinch nutmeg
1	piece cinnamon stick
1	clove
1/2	cup sugar

Finely pare the rind of the lemon and juice it. Place the water, lemon rind and juice, nutmeg, cinnamon stick, clove and sugar into a pan. Bring to a boil, stirring to dissolve the sugar. Gently heat for 15 minutes without boiling. Strain the liquid and return to the pan. Serve hot in mugs or tea glasses. Warming after skiing or other cold weather activities.

Notes: Good source of Vitamin C.

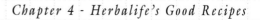

Herbal All-Bran Shake

2	tablespoons All-Bran Cereal
2	tablespoons skim dry milk
1/4	cup warm water
2	tablespoons Formula 1 French Vanilla

Serves: 1
Prep Time: 0:05

Combine the dry ingredients and stir in the water. Adjust the consistency to taste. Serve chilled for breakfast, garnished with fresh strawberry slices.

Notes: Excellent source of Vitamin C, B6, B12, B1, B2, Folacin, Calcium, Iron and Zinc. Good source of Vitamin A and Niacin.

Total Calories 160
Protein 15g
Carbohydrate 26g
Fat 1g
Cholesterol 3mg
Dietary Fiber 6g
% Calories from
Fat 5%

Iced Tea

6	teaspoons Darjeeling tea
1	tablespoon sugar
4	cups boiling water

Serves: 4
Prep Time: 0:05
Stand Time: 0:30+

Warm a teapot with hot water then empty it. Place the tea and sugar in the bottom of the pot and cover with rapidly boiling water. Allow to stand for 5 minutes, then strain into a pitcher. Let cool and serve chilled, garnished with slices of lemon or sprigs of fresh mint.

Total Calories 12
Protein 0g
Carbohydrate 3g
Fat 0g
Cholesterol 0mg
Dietary Fiber 0g
% Calories from
Fat 0%

Italian Soda Shake

3	fluid ounces orange juice
3	fluid ounces soda water
3	fluid ounces skim milk
2	tablespoons Formula 1 French Vanilla
2	tablespoons Herbal Aloe

Serves: 1
Prep Time: 0:05

Total Calories 153
Protein 12g
Carbohydrate 24g
Fat 1g
Cholesterol 2mg
Dietary Fiber 3g
% Calories from
Fat 6%

Place all the ingredients in a blender and blend until smooth. Serve chilled, garnished with thin strips of orange peel and a sprig of mint.

Notes: Excellent source of Vitamin C, B6, B1, B2, Iron and Zinc. Good source of Folacin and Calcium.

Kiwi Quencher

2	tablespoons Formula 1 French Vanilla
8	fluid ounces water
1	kiwi fruit
1/2	banana
3	ice cubes
2	drops green chartreuse

Serves: 1
Prep Time: 0:05

Total Calories 80
Protein 8g
Carbohydrate 10g
Fat <1g
Cholesterol 0mg
Dietary Fiber 3g
% Calories from
Fat 7%

Combine ingredients in a blender. Serve chilled with a slice of kiwi fruit as garnish.

Notes: Excellent source of Vitamin C, B6, B2, Iron and Zinc. Good source of Vitamin B1.

Lemonade

4	lemons
2	tablespoons sugar
2	cups water

Peel two of the lemons as thinly as possible. Halve the others and juice them. Strain the juice into a pitcher and add the lemon rind and sugar. Pour boiling water onto the lemon and leave to stand until cold. Serve chilled, garnished with slices of lemon.

Notes: Excellent source of Vitamin C.

Serves: 4
Prep Time: 0:10

Total Calories 45
Protein 1g
Carbohydrate 18g
Fat 1g
Cholesterol 0mg
Dietary Fiber 1g
% Calories from
Fat 4%

Melon Masterpiece

2	tablespoons Formula 1 Tropical Fruit
8	fluid ounces water
1/2	cup fresh mango pieces
1/2	cup fresh cantaloupe pieces
3	ice cubes

Combine all ingredients in a blender. Serve chilled garnish with a sprig of fresh mint.

Notes: Excellent source of Vitamins A, C, Iron and Zinc. Good source of Vitamin B6 and Folacin.

Serves: 1
Prep Time: 0:05

Total Calories 162
Protein 9g
Carbohydrate 31g
Fat 1g
Cholesterol 0mg
Dietary Fiber 5g
% Calories from
Fat 5%

Mango Special

Serves: 8
Prep Time: 0:10

Total Calories 70
Protein 1g
Carbohydrate 18g
Fat 3g
Cholesterol 0mg
Dietary Fiber 1g
% Calories from Fat
3%

2	cups mangos diced
2	cups orange juice
2	tablespoons sugar
1/4	cup lime juice
1/4	cup lemon juice
2	cups water
3	ice cubes

Combine the ingredients in a blender. Strain and serve in a pitcher either for breakfast or as a non-alcoholic cocktail. This is excellent with champagne.

Notes: Excellent source of Vitamin C and A.
Good source of Folacin.

Mocha Shake

Serves: 1
Prep Time: 0:05

Total Calories 228
Protein 17g
Carbohydrate 39g
Fat 1g
Cholesterol 4mg
Dietary Fiber 4g
% Calories from
Fat 5%

2	tablespoons Formula 1 Dutch Chocolate
1/2	teaspoon instant coffee
8	fluid ounces skim milk
1/2	medium banana
3	ice cubes

Combine the ingredients in a blender. Serve chilled, garnished with a few chocolate sprinkles or a chocolate coated coffee bean.

Notes: Excellent source of Vitamin C, B6, B12, B1, B2, Calcium and Zinc. Good source of Vitamin A, Folacin and Iron.

Mulled Cider

2	quarts apple cider
1	orange, sliced
1	lemon
4	cinnamon sticks
4	whole cloves
1/2	teaspoon nutmeg
1/2	teaspoon ginger

Serves: 16
Prep Time: 0:50

Total Calories 58
Protein 1g
Carbohydrate 15g
Fat 1g
Cholesterol 0mg
Dietary Fiber 1g
% Calories from
Fat 2%

Combine all the ingredients in a large pan. Bring to a boil, then simmer for 40 minutes. Strain the cider and serve hot.

Orange Blossom Shake

2	tablespoons Formula 1 French Vanilla
1/2	teaspoon orange extract
8	fluid ounces skim milk
1/2	orange
3	ice cubes

Serves: 1
Prep Time: 0:05

Total Calories 168
Protein 16g
Carbohydrate 22g
Fat 1g
Cholesterol 4mg
Dietary Fiber 3g
% Calories from
Fat 6%

Combine ingredients in a blender and serve chilled, garnished with a slice of orange.

Notes: Excellent source of Vitamin C, B6, B12, B1, B2, Calcium, Iron and Zinc. Good source of Vitamin A.

Orange Dreamsicle Delight

2	tablespoons Formula 1 French Vanilla
8	fluid ounces orange juice
3	ice cubes

Serves: 1
Prep Time: 0:05

Total Calories 192
Protein 10g
Carbohydrate 37g
Fat 1g
Cholesterol 0mg
Dietary Fiber 3g
% Calories from
Fat 5%

Combine ingredients in a blender. Garnish with a wedge of fresh orange and a sprig of fresh mint.

Notes: Excellent source of Vitamin C, B6, B1, B2, Folacin, Iron and Zinc. Good source of Vitamin A.

Passionate Papaya Shake

2	tablespoons Formula 1 French Vanilla
1/2	papaya
6	fluid ounces apple juice
2	fluid ounces Herbal Aloe
dash	cinnamon

Serves: 1
Prep Time: 0:05

Total Calories 256
Protein 10g
Carbohydrate 54g
Fat 1g
Cholesterol 0mg
Dietary Fiber 6g
% Calories from
Fat 4%

Blend together and serve chilled.

Notes: Excellent source of Vitamin C, B6, B1, B2, Folacin, Iron and Zinc. Good source of Vitamin A.

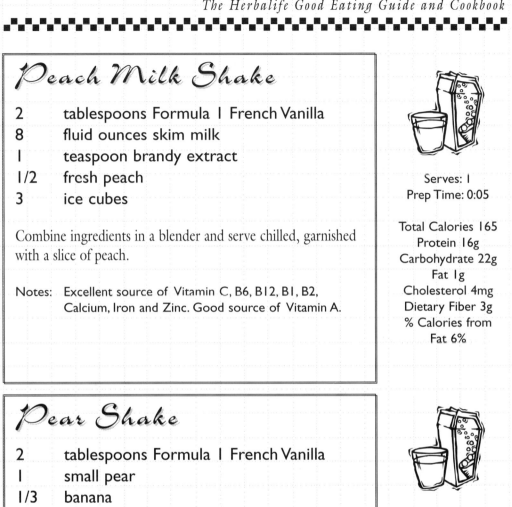

Peach Milk Shake

2	tablespoons Formula 1 French Vanilla
8	fluid ounces skim milk
1	teaspoon brandy extract
1/2	fresh peach
3	ice cubes

Combine ingredients in a blender and serve chilled, garnished with a slice of peach.

Notes: Excellent source of Vitamin C, B6, B12, B1, B2, Calcium, Iron and Zinc. Good source of Vitamin A.

Serves: 1
Prep Time: 0:05

Total Calories 165
Protein 16g
Carbohydrate 22g
Fat 1g
Cholesterol 4mg
Dietary Fiber 3g
% Calories from Fat 6%

Pear Shake

2	tablespoons Formula 1 French Vanilla
1	small pear
1/3	banana
4	ounces Herbal Aloe
2	drops almond extract
dash	cinnamon

Blend together and serve chilled.

Notes: Excellent source of Vitamin C, B6, B1, B2, Iron and Zinc. Good source of Folacin.

Serves: 1
Prep Time: 0:05

Total Calories 258
Protein 10g
Carbohydrate 55g
Fat 2g
Cholesterol 0mg
Dietary Fiber 8g
% Calories from Fat 6%

Prune Shake

2	tablespoons Formula 1 French Vanilla
6	fluid ounces prune juice
2	fluid ounces Herbal Aloe

Blend the Formula 1 with the prune juice and Herbal Aloe. Serve chilled.

Notes: Excellent source of Vitamin C, B6, B1, B2, Iron and Zinc. Good source of Niacin.

Serves: 1
Prep Time: 0:05

Total Calories 216
Protein 9g
Carbohydrate 44g
Fat 1g
Cholesterol 0mg
Dietary Fiber 4g
% Calories from Fat 3%

Raspberry RazMaTaz

2	tablespoons Formula 1 Dutch Chocolate
8	fluid ounces water
1/3	cup raspberries, fresh or frozen
1/2	banana
3	ice cubes

Combine all ingredients in a blender. Serve chilled, garnished with fresh raspberries and a sprig of mint.

Notes: Excellent source of Vitamin C and Folacin.

Serves: 1
Prep Time: 0:05

Total Calories 162
Protein 9g
Carbohydrate 32g
Fat <1g
Cholesterol 5mg
Dietary Fiber 7g
% Calories from Fat 5%

Sangria

1	lemon
2	oranges
1	apple
4	fluid ounces brandy
24	fluid ounces red wine
12	fluid ounces soda water
2	tablespoons sugar

Serves: 12
Prep Time: 0:05

Total Calories 90
Protein <1g
Carbohydrate 9g
Fat 1g
Cholesterol 0mg
Dietary Fiber 1g
% Calories from
Fat 3%

Place about 8-10 ice cubes in the base of a large bowl. Add the lemon, oranges and apples cut into even sized pieces. Sprinkle the fruit with the sugar. Stir in the brandy, red wine and finally the soda water. Stir well and serve with a large ladle. This drink tastes great with a barbecue and meals alfresco.

Notes: Excellent source of Vitamin C.

Soda Fountain Shake

2	tablespoons Formula 1 French Vanilla
5	fluid ounces skim milk
3	fluid ounces diet soda
1/2	banana
3	ice cubes

Serves: 1
Prep Time: 0:05

Total Calories 133
Protein 13g
Carbohydrate 18g
Fat 1g
Cholesterol 2mg
Dietary Fiber 3g
% Calories from
Fat 6%

Blend together and serve chilled. Banana may be substituted with peach. Garnish with a slice of banana.

Notes: Excellent source of Vitamin C, B6, B1, B2, Calcium, Iron and Zinc.

Spicy Tomato Juice

2	cups tomato juice
1	teaspoon Tabasco sauce
1	teaspoon fresh lemon juice
2	stalks celery
	pinch salt
	pinch sugar

Serves: 2
Prep Time: 0:10

Total Calories 133
Protein 13g
Carbohydrate 18g
Fat 1g
Cholesterol 0mg
Dietary Fiber 3g
% Calories from
Fat 6%

Combine all the ingredients in a jug. Chill for 30 minutes and serve garnished with celery stalks.

Notes: Excellent source of Vitamin A, C, Folacin. Good source of Vitamin B1 and Niacin.

Strawberry Daiquiri

6	fluid ounces rum
1/2	cup fresh lime juice
2	tablespoons sugar
4	cups strawberries
6	ice cubes

Combine rum, lime juice, sugar and ice cubes in a blender. Add the strawberries after the sugar has dissolved and continue to blend at high speed until the mixture is smooth. Serve with sugar around the rim of each glass.

Notes: Excellent source of Vitamin C. Good source of Folacin.

Serves: 4
Prep Time: 0:10

Total Calories 173
Protein 1g
Carbohydrate 20g
Fat 1g
Cholesterol 0mg
Dietary Fiber 4g
% Calories from
Fat 6%

Strawberry Sensation

2	tablespoons Formula 1 Wild Berry
8	fluid ounces water
1	cup strawberries
1	apricot
3	ice cubes

Combine all ingredients in a blender. Garnish with a strawberry and sprig of fresh mint.

Notes: Excellent source of Vitamin C, B6, B1, B2, Iron and Zinc. Good source of Folacin and Calcium.

Serves: 1
Prep Time: 0:05

Total Calories 124
Protein 9g
Carbohydrate 21g
Fat 2g
Cholesterol 0mg
Dietary Fiber 6g
% Calories from
Fat 11%

Vanilla Shake

2	tablespoons Formula 1 French Vanilla
6	fluid ounces skim milk
3	ice cubes
4	ounces nonfat yogurt

Serves: 1
Prep Time: 0:05

Total Calories 228
Protein 23g
Carbohydrate 31g
Fat 1g
Cholesterol 6mg
Dietary Fiber 3g
% Calories from
Fat 5%

Blend all ingredients together. Serve chilled, garnished with fresh fruit.

Notes: Excellent source of Vitamin B6, B12, B2, Calcium and Zinc. Good source of Vitamin C, B1 and Iron.

Wild Berry-Orange Shake

2	tablespoons Formula 1 Wild Berry
8	fluid ounces orange juice
4	strawberries
3	ice cubes

Serves: 1
Prep Time: 0:05

Total Calories 192
Protein 10g
Carbohydrate 36g
Fat 2g
Cholesterol 0mg
Dietary Fiber 3g
% Calories from
Fat 7%

Combine all ingredients in a blender and serve chilled, garnished with a fresh strawberry.

Notes: Excellent source of Vitamin C, B6, B1, B2, Folacin, Iron and Zinc. Good source of Vitamin A and Calcium.

Breads, Cookies, Cakes and Pies

Serves: 10
Prep Time: 0:20
Baking time:0:30

Total Calories 219
Protein 6g
Carbohydrate 48g
Fat <1g
Cholesterol 0mg
Dietary Fiber <1g
% Calories from
Fat <1%

Angel Food Cake

1 1/2	cups flour, cake, sifted
1 3/4	cups sugar
14	egg whites
1/4	teaspoon salt
2	teaspoons vanilla extract
1	teaspoon fresh lemon juice

Preheat the oven to 300 °F. Beat the egg whites (which should be at room temperature) until fluffy but not dry. Fold the sugar with a metal spoon into the egg whites and then lightly fold in the sifted flour. Add the vanilla extract and lemon juice. Pour into an 8" diameter cake pan or a 10" tube pan. Smooth the top and place in the middle of the oven. Bake until a pale color and the top is spongy. A toothpick should come out clean. Cool in the pan and remove to place on a serving dish by releasing with a palette knife. Serve with fresh fruit and nonfat yogurt or ice cream.

Notes: Good source of Vitamin B1 and B2.

Apricot Almond Squares

1	cup dried apricot halves
1/2	cup almonds, dry-roasted, ground
2	tablespoons butter
1/4	cup of oatmeal
1/4	cup sugar
1	teaspoon vanilla extract
1/2	teaspoon almond extract
1/2	teaspoon salt
1	cup flour
1/2	cup egg substitute, liquid
1	cup firmly packed light brown sugar
1/2	teaspoon baking powder
1	tablespoon confectioner's sugar

Serves: 36
Prep Time: 0:10
Baking time: 0:50

Total Calories 67
Protein 1g
Carbohydrate 13g
Fat 1g
Cholesterol 0mg
Dietary Fiber 1g
% Calories from
Fat 15%

Preheat the oven to 350°F. Place apricots in a pan of cold water and bring to a boil. Cover and simmer for 6-8 minutes. Drain and pat dry. Slice thinly, cover and set aside. Blend the butter and oatmeal with 2 tablespoons water. Mix in 1/2 of the flour and the ground almonds with a metal spoon. Spread over the bottom of a 9" baking pan. Bake for 20 minutes. While the pastry is baking, sift the rest of the flour with the baking powder and salt. Lightly beat the egg substitute with the brown sugar and blend in the flour mixture. Add the vanilla and almond extracts and stir in the apricots. Spread over the pastry. Bake for 30 minutes until brown. Cool and sift confectioner's sugar over the squares before serving.

Apricot and Strawberry Cake

Serves: 8
Prep Time: 0:10
Baking time: 0:35

Total Calories 465
Protein 9g
Carbohydrate 106g
Fat 2g
Cholesterol 54mg
Dietary Fiber 4g
% Calories from
Fat 4%

2 3/4	cups flour
2 1/2	teaspoons baking powder
1 3/4	cups sugar
1 1/4	cups skim milk
3/4	cup apricots, puréed
2	eggs, beaten
1 1/2	teaspoons vanilla
9	tablespoons strawberry preserves
8	large strawberries, sliced thin
2	tablespoons apricot brandy glaze

Preheat the oven to 375°F. Sift the flour, baking powder and sugar in a mixing bowl and stir to blend. Using a metal spoon combine the skim milk, apricot purée, eggs and vanilla with the dry ingredients. Pour the batter into two 8" cake pans sprayed with oil. Bake for 25 - 30 minutes or until a toothpick comes out dry from the center. Let the cake cool in the pan for 5 minutes before removing and cooling on a rack. Split each cake in half horizontally and fill with strawberry preserves. Brush the apricot brandy glaze on the top and arrange strawberry slices in a petal-shaped pattern on the top. Glaze the strawberry slices also and serve with fresh whipped cream; low or nonfat yogurt or ice cream.

Notes: Excellent source of Vitamin C, B1 and B2. Good
source of Vitamin A, Folacin, Niacin, Calcium and Iron.
Good source of Vitamin A, B6 and Zinc.

Banana Bread

2	medium bananas
3	egg whites
2	tablespoons canola oil
1/2	teaspoon ground cinnamon
1/2	teaspoon ground nutmeg
1	tablespoon honey
1 1/2	cups flour
2	teaspoons baking powder
1/2	teaspoon salt

Serves: 10
Prep Time: 0:10
Baking time: 1:00

Total Calories 121
Protein 2g
Carbohydrate 22g
Fat 3g
Cholesterol 0mg
Dietary Fiber 1g
% Calories from
Fat 22%

Preheat the oven to 350°F. Lightly grease a 9 X 5 loaf pan. Beat the egg whites until fluffy, but not dry. Mash the bananas with the honey and canola oil and fold into the egg whites. In another bowl, sift the flour and salt. Add the baking powder, ground cinnamon and nutmeg. Combine with the banana mixture using light, firm strokes. Place the batter into the loaf pan and bake for 50 to 60 minutes or until a toothpick comes out clean. Cool for 10 minutes before turning out. Slice and serve warm or cold.

Notes: Good source of Vitamin B1.
Variations: Add 8 apricot halves, finely chopped OR 1/2 cups golden raisins OR 1/3 cup pecans or English walnuts, chopped.

Banana Cream Pie

2   tablespoons Formula 1 French Vanilla
1   cup skim milk
1   tablespoon banana pudding

Blend together and serve chilled, topped with banana slices and crumbled graham crackers.

Notes: Excellent source of Vitamin A, C, B6, B12, B1, B2,
           Calcium, Iron and Zinc. Good source of Vitamin A.

Serves: 1
Prep Time: 0:10

Total Calories 183
Protein 17g
Carbohydrate 25g
Fat 1g
Cholesterol 6mg
Dietary Fiber 3g
% Calories from
Fat 7%

Carrot Cake

2	tablespoons unsalted butter
1 1/2	cups sugar
1	cup egg substitute, liquid
2	cups flour
2	teaspoons baking soda
2	teaspoons ground cinnamon
1/2	teaspoon ground allspice
1/4	teaspoon ground nutmeg
1/4	teaspoon ground cloves
4	large carrots finely grated
1	cup English walnuts chopped
1/2	cup golden raisins

Serves: 10
Prep Time: 0:10
Baking time: 1:00

Total Calories 363
Protein 8g
Carbohydrate 60g
Fat 10g
Cholesterol 7mg
Dietary Fiber 2g
% Calories from
Fat 25%

Preheat oven to 350 °F. Combine the butter and sugar in a mixing bowl and beat until light and fluffy. Add the egg substitute and continue to beat. Fold in the sifted flour, baking soda, ground cinnamon, allspice, nutmeg and cloves into the mixture. Stir in the grated carrots, English walnuts and golden raisins. Adjust the consistency by adding a little water or skim milk if necessary so that the batter drops off the spoon to the count of 3. Spread the batter into a 9" baking pan and bake for 55 minutes or until a toothpick comes out clean. Cool in the pan for 10 minutes, then turn out onto a wire rack and cool completely. Serve with optional cream cheese topping .

Notes: Excellent source of Vitamin A and B1. Good source of Vitamin B2, Folacin, Niacin and Iron.

Chocolate Chip Cookies

2	cups flour, all-purpose
1	teaspoon baking powder
1	teaspoon salt
8	ounces chocolate chips
1	teaspoon vanilla extract
1/2	cup egg substitute, liquid
3/4	cup apple sauce, unsweetened
1/2	cup brown sugar, packed

Serves: 36
Prep Time: 0:10
Baking time: 0:10

Total Calories 103
Protein 1g
Carbohydrate 13g
Fat 2g
Cholesterol 10mg
Dietary Fiber 1g
% Calories from
Fat 25%

Preheat the oven to 375°F. Combine the apple sauce and sugar until light and fluffy. Add the vanilla extract and the beaten egg substitute (or 2 whole eggs). In a separate bowl, sift the flour and salt, add the baking powder and lightly blend into the apple sauce and egg mixture. Stir in the chocolate chips. Place rounded teaspoonfuls of the batter onto a baking sheet and bake for 8 to 10 minutes. Cool on a wire rack and serve warm.

Variations: 1/2 cup of chopped pecans or English walnuts.
1/2 cup of white chocolate chips.

Currant Scones

1 1/2	cups flour, all-purpose
1/2	teaspoon baking soda
1/2	teaspoon cream of tartar
	pinch salt
1	tablespoon sugar
2	tablespoons butter
1/2	cup buttermilk
2	tablespoons golden seedless raisins

Serves: 8
Prep Time: 0:10
Baking time: 0:30

Total Calories 130
Protein 3g
Carbohydrate 22g
Fat 3g
Cholesterol 8mg
Dietary Fiber <1g
% Calories from
Fat 22%

Preheat the oven to 375 °F. Cut the butter into small pieces and add to the sifted flour, baking soda and cream of tartar (or one teaspoon baking powder) Add the sugar and combine with a food processor or by lightly rubbing with your hands until it is bread crumb consistency. Add the raisins. Add sufficient buttermilk to make a soft, elastic dough. Turn onto a floured pastry board, knead lightly and roll out to about 1/4" thickness. Cut in circles and place on a greased and flour-dusted baking tray. Also dust the top of the scones with a little flour. Bake for 25-30 minutes. Cool on a wire rack and serve warm or cold with tea or coffee.

Notes: Good source of Vitamin B1. A beaten egg may be added to the milk to make a richer recipe.

Ginger Cookies

1/2	cup apple sauce substitute
1	cup butter
1 3/4	cups sugar
3/4	cup brown sugar
1	medium egg
1/3	cup molasses
2 3/4	cups white flour
1 1/4	teaspoons baking soda
10 1/2	teaspoons cinnamon
2	tablespoons ginger
1	tablespoon cloves
1	tablespoon nutmeg
1/2	teaspoon salt
1/2	cup powdered sugar

Serves: 36
Prep Time: 0:20

Total Calories 109
Protein 1g
Carbohydrate 25g
Fat 1g
Cholesterol 7mg
Dietary Fiber 4g
% Calories from
Fat 3%

Preheat the oven to 350°F. Cream butter and sugar together until light and fluffy, taking about 8 to 10 minutes by hand or 4 to 5 minutes in a food processor. Lightly fold in the beaten egg and molasses. Sift flour, baking soda and salt and lightly fold into the mixture with firm strokes using a metal spoon. Season with the cinnamon, ginger, cloves, nutmeg and salt. Form 3/4" round balls of dough, flatten a little and dip the top into 1/2 cup of powdered sugar. Place on a non-stick cookie sheet with the sugar side up. Bake for 12 to 15 minutes depending upon how crisp you like them. Serve warm.

Key Lime Pie

1	cup Graham cracker crumbs
2	tablespoons unsalted butter
1	tablespoon water
1	envelope gelatin powder, unsweetened
6	tablespoons fresh lime juice
1/2	cup sugar
1/2	teaspoon vanilla extract
2	cups nonfat yogurt
1	tablespoon lime rind, grated

Serves: 6
Prep Time: 0:20
Stand Time: 1:00

Total Calories 253
Protein 18g
Carbohydrate 35g
Fat 6g
Cholesterol 12mg
Dietary Fiber 1g
% Calories from
Fat 19%

Mix the Graham cracker crumbs with the butter and line an 8" baking pan. Dissolve the gelatin powder in the water and add the lime juice and sugar. Heat in a small saucepan until the sugar is dissolved. Allow to cool and add the yogurt and lime rind. When beginning to thicken, place on top of the crumbs and leave to set. Garnish with sugared lemon rind. Serve chilled.

Notes: Good source of Vitamin C, B2 and Calcium.

Muffins

1 1/2	cups whole-grain wheat flour
1/2	cup all-purpose flour
1/ 2	teaspoon salt
3	teaspoons baking powder
1	beaten egg
2	tablespoons brown sugar
2	tablespoons canola oil

Serves: 12
Prep Time: 0:05
Baking times: 0:30

Total Calories 102
Protein 3g
Carbohydrate 17g
Fat 3g
Cholesterol 18mg
Dietary Fiber 2g
% Calories from
Fat 25%

Preheat the oven to 400°F. Lightly beat the egg and add the milk, honey and canola oil. Sift the flour with the salt and baking powder. Lightly fold the dry ingredients into the liquid with a metal spoon. Oil muffin tins or use paper containers. Fill the containers and bake for 20 to 30 minutes until risen and brown on top.

Peanut Butter Sesame Seed Bars

1/2	cup Formula 1 French Vanilla
3/4	cup skim dry milk
1	cup dry oatmeal flakes
3/4	cup low-fat peanut butter
1/2	cup honey
2	tablespoons warm water
2	tablespoons sesame seeds

Serves: 12
Prep Time: 0:05
Stand Time: 0:30

Total Calories 143
Protein 9g
Carbohydrate 25g
Fat 2g
Cholesterol 1mg
Dietary Fiber 2g
% Calories from
Fat 9%

Combine all of the ingredients in a mixing bowl. Spray a 9 X 9 baking pan with oil and press the mixture into the pan. Refrigerate for at least 30 minutes before cutting into brownie shaped bars.

Notes: Excellent source of Vitamin B6, B1, B2, Folacin, Niacin and Zinc. Good source of Vitamin A, Calcium and Iron.

Pineapple Meringue Pie

I	cup pineapple chunks in light syrup
I	cup pineapple juice
I	tablespoon butter
I	tablespoon flour
I	egg yolk
1/2	cup sugar
2	egg whites

Serves: 6
Prep Time: 0:20

Total Calories 146
Protein 2.1g
Carbohydrate 29g
Fat 3g
Cholesterol 41mg
Dietary Fiber 1g
% Calories from
Fat 17%

Preheat the oven to 350°F. Drain the pineapple chunks and retain the light syrup. Melt the butter in a saucepan and add the flour. Stir over a gentle heat for 2-3 minutes until a roux forms and the mixture comes away from the sides easily. Add the syrup and pineapple juice (total of one cup) and bring to a boil, stirring all the time. When the sauce is thickened, add the egg yolk and all of the pineapple chunks except one or two for decoration. Remove from the heat and pour into a greased 9" pie dish. Beat the egg whites until fluffy but not dry. Fold in the sugar and continue to beat until shiny and stiff. Spoon over the pineapple mixture and garnish with the left over pineapple chunks. Place in the oven for 3-4 minutes until the top has browned. Serve hot.

Notes: Excellent source of Vitamin C.

Soda Bread

3	cups whole-grain wheat flour
1	cup all-purpose flour
2	tablespoons sugar
2	teaspoons baking powder
1 1/2	teaspoons baking soda
1	teaspoon salt
2	tablespoons butter
1 1/2	cups buttermilk

Serves: 16
Prep Time: 0:10
Baking Time: 1:00

Total Calories 132
Protein 5g
Carbohydrate 25g
Fat 2g
Cholesterol 5mg
Dietary Fiber 3g
% Calories from
Fat 13%

Sift flour and combine with the other dry ingredients in a large bowl. Cut the butter into small pieces and crumble by lightly lifting the mixture and rubbing the butter. You may use a pastry blender. Turn onto a floured wooden board and knead a few times until smooth. Keep your hands cool as you do this. Heat the oven to 350°F. Grease a baking sheet with butter and place the dough in the middle. Flatten the top a little and make a cross shaped incision in the dough. Bake for about one hour until the bread is cooked through. Test with a skewer or toothpick; if it comes out clean it is cooked. Serve hot with a main dish.

Notes: Good source of Vitamin B1 and Folacin.

Wheatmeal Bread

Serves: 20
Prep Time: 0:20
Baking Time: 0:30

Total Calories 50
Protein 2g
Carbohydrate 9g
Fat <1g
Cholesterol 2mg
Dietary Fiber 1g
% Calories from
Fat 13%

1	cup all-purpose flour
1	cup whole-grain wheat flour
2	teaspoons salt
1	tablespoon butter
1	teaspoon sugar
2	teaspoons yeast
1	cup water

Preheat the oven to 450°F. Prepare 2 loaf pans (9 X 5) by lightly greasing with butter. Sift the flours and mix with the salt in a large bowl. Add the butter and rub into a crumb texture. Dissolve the sugar in hot water and add the yeast. Set aside until frothy (about 10 minutes). Mix the yeast into the dough until it leaves the sides of the bowl clean. Turn out onto a pastry board and knead for 10 minutes or use a dough hook with a food processor. Divide the dough into 2 pieces. With each piece, form 4 balls by pulling the dough up and round 4 corners in your hand, dusted with a little flour. Place 4 balls in each of the 2 loaf pans. Brush the top of the loaves with salt water and sprinkle with cracked wheat. Place the loaves in a plastic bag and tie loosely. Leave in a warm place until the dough rises above the tops of the pans. Bake for 30 minutes. Remove from the loaf pans and cool on a wire tray.

Notes: Makes 2 loaves.

Zucchini Bread

1	cup shredded zucchini
1	cup sugar
1/2	cup applesauce
1	teaspoon vanilla extract
1/2	cup crushed pineapple, drained
1 1/2	cups flour
1	teaspoon baking soda
1/2	teaspoon salt
1/4	teaspoon baking powder
1	teaspoon ground cinnamon
1/2	teaspoon ground nutmeg
1/2	teaspoon ground allspice
1/2	cup finely chopped English walnuts

Serves: 12
Prep Time: :10
Baking Time: 1:00

Total Calories 171
Protein 3g
Carbohydrate 34g
Fat 3g
Cholesterol 0mg
Dietary Fiber 1g
% Calories from
Fat 17%

Preheat the oven to 350°F. Lightly grease a 9 X 5 loaf pan.
Beat the egg whites in a bowl until stiff but not dry. Beat in
the sugar, applesauce and vanilla. Stir in the zucchini and
pineapple. In a separate bowl, sift the flour and salt. Add the
baking powder, baking soda, ground cinnamon, nutmeg and
allspice. Add to the zucchini mixture, using a few brisk
movement of the spoon. Place the batter into the loaf pan and
bake for 50 to 60 minutes or until a toothpick comes out
clean. Let the loaf cool in the pan for 10 minutes before
turning out onto a wire rack to cool completely. Serve warm
or cold. Delicious for picnics.

Notes: Good source of Vitamin B1.

Desserts, Fruit and Ices

Serves: 8
Prep Time: 0:15
Baking Time: 0:45

Total Calories 266
Protein 3g
Carbohydrate 56g
Fat 1g
Cholesterol 7mg
Dietary Fiber 2g
% Calories from
Fat 3%

Apple Crisp

5	large apples
1	tablespoon sugar
1/2	teaspoon ground cinnamon
2	cups flour
1	cup light brown sugar
3/4	cup butter substitute

Preheat the oven to 350°F. Peel, slice and core the apples and place in a shallow ovenproof dish. Sprinkle with sugar and cinnamon. Mix the butter into the flour and sugar with a mixer or with your fingers. The crisp topping should have the consistency of fine crumbs. Lay the topping over the apples and bake in the oven for 45 minutes. Serve hot with whipped cream or vanilla ice cream.

Notes: Excellent source of Vitamin B1. Good source of
Vitamin A, B2, Niacin and Iron.

Brownies

1	cup liquid egg substitute, beaten
4	ounces unsweetened chocolate, chopped
1/2	cup butter substitute
1 1/2	cups sugar
2	teaspoons vanilla extract
3/4	cup flour
1	cup chopped English walnuts
	pinch salt

Serves: 16
Prep Time: 0:05
Baking Time: 0:30

Total Calories 202
Protein 4g
Carbohydrate 27g
Fat 9g
Cholesterol 2mg
Dietary Fiber 2g
% Calories from
Fat 40%

Preheat the oven to 350°F. Line an 8" baking pan with parchment paper. Melt the chocolate and butter in a heavy bottomed pan over low heat and let cool. Add sugar to beaten egg substitute and flavor with vanilla. Sift flour and salt and fold in with a metal spoon. Add the chocolate mixture and the nuts. Place in the baking pan and bake for 30 minutes or until a toothpick comes out clean. Cool in the pan and serve either chilled or at room temperature.

Notes: Good source of Vitamin A. Refrigerate for at least 2 hours for easier cutting.

Fresh Fruit Salad

Serves: 4
Prep Time: 0:20
Stand Time: 1:00

Total Calories 320
Protein 4g
Carbohydrate 82g
Fat 1g
Cholesterol 0mg
Dietary Fiber 8g
% Calories from
Fat 3%

1	apple, peeled and chopped
8	small seedless grapes, peeled
1	can mandarin oranges in light syrup
1	plum, pitted and chopped
1	nectarine, pitted and chopped
1/2	banana, peeled and sliced
1	pear, peeled and chopped
2	tablespoons fresh lemon juice

Combine all of the ingredients in a mixing bowl. Chill in the refrigerator for at least one hour. Transfer to individual dessert dishes and serve garnished with tiny sprigs of mint or borage.

Notes: Excellent source of Vitamin C, A, B6 and Iron. Good source of Vitamin B1, B2 and Folacin.

Fresh Peaches in Lemon Juice

6   fresh peaches, peeled and sliced
2   lemons, juiced
2   tablespoons sugar

Arrange peach slices in a serving dish and cover with the sugar and lemon juice. Leave for at least 2 hours in the refrigerator. The peaches will leach juice into the lemon juice and create a sweet sauce with the sugar. This is best served at room temperature after a main course of meat to clean the palate.

Notes: Excellent source of Vitamin C. Good source of Vitamin A.

Serves: 4
Prep Time: 0:05
Stand Time: 2:00

Total Calories 91
Protein 2g
Carbohydrate 26g
Fat <1g
Cholesterol 0g
Dietary Fiber 3g
% Calories from
Fat 2%

Fruit Popsicles

1	cup nonfat yogurt
1/2	cup orange juice
1/2	cup mandarin oranges
2	tablespoons Formula 1 French Vanilla
1	drop Kindermins
1/2	teaspoon chocolate syrup

Serves: 4
Prep Time: 0:30

Total Calories 78
Protein 6g
Carbohydrate 13g
Fat <1g
Cholesterol 1mg
Dietary Fiber 1g
% Calories from
Fat 4%

Combine ingredients together and place in 4 ounce decorated Dixie cups. Place pieces of foil over the top and insert popsicle sticks into the cups through foil. Freeze and serve as a healthy frozen treat. Kids love them (old and young!). The cups can be carried and used to keep the popsicle from dripping as they melt.

Notes: Good source of Vitamin A, B1, B2, Niacin, B6, B12, Folacin. Good source of Calcium.

Lemon Sherbet

2	large egg whites
2 1/2	cups sugar
1	cup water
1 1/2	cups fresh lemon juice
1	teaspoon grated lemon peel

Serves: 12
Prep Time: 0:15

Total Calories 171
Protein 1g
Carbohydrate 44g
Fat 0g
Cholesterol 0mg
Dietary Fiber <1g
% Calories from
Fat 0%

Dissolve the sugar in the water over gentle heat, stirring constantly. When the sugar is dissolved, bring to a boil and boil for 1-2 minutes. Cool. Beat the egg whites till fluffy, but not dry. Slowly drizzle the warm syrup into the egg whites and add the lemon juice and grated peel. Transfer to an ice cream making machine and follow the manufacturer's instructions.

Notes: Excellent source of Vitamin C.

Mixed Berry Sherbet

2	cups sugar
1	cup water
4	cups berries
2	teaspoons fresh lemon juice

Serves: 12
Prep Time: 0:15+

Total Calories 143
Protein 1g
Carbohydrate 37g
Fat <1g
Cholesterol 0mg
Dietary Fiber 1g
% Calories from
Fat 1%

Dissolve the sugar in the water in a pan over gentle heat. When the sugar is fully dissolved, bring the water to a boil and boil fast for 1-2 minutes. Do not allow the syrup to turn color. Cool. Blend the berries and add the lemon juice. Transfer to an ice cream making machine and follow the manufacturer's instructions.

Notes: Excellent source of Vitamin C.

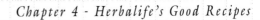

Peach Crumble

1	tablespoon fresh lemon juice
4	large fresh peaches
1/2	cup sugar
1/2	cup whole-grain wheat flour
1/2	teaspoon cinnamon
2	tablespoons brown sugar
1	tablespoon butter

Serves: 8
Prep Time: 0:10
Baking time: 0:45

Total Calories 114
Protein 1g
Carbohydrate 25g
Fat 2g
Cholesterol 4mg
Dietary Fiber 2g
% Calories from
Fat 11%

Preheat the oven to 375°F. Peel, pit and slice the peaches. Cover with lemon juice to prevent them from turning brown. Combine the peach slices with the sugar and place them in the base of an ovenproof dish. Mix the brown sugar, flour and cinnamon together in a large bowl and add the butter cut into small pieces. Combine well. Sprinkle on top of the fruit and bake for 45 minutes. Serve hot.

Notes: This may be made with other seasonal fruit such as apples, pears, apricots, plums or nectarines.

Peach Frozen Yogurt

2	tablespoons sugar
32	ounces plain low-fat yogurt
I	cup frozen peach slices
I	tablespoon fresh lime juice

Serves: 12
Prep Time: 0:15+

Total Calories 196
Protein 4g
Carbohydrate 44g
Fat 1g
Cholesterol 5mg
Dietary Fiber 1g
% Calories from
Fat 5%

Whisk the sugar into the yogurt until completely dissolved (about 2 minutes). Add the lime juice. Put the peach slices into the blender and blend. Combine with the yogurt and transfer the mixture to an ice cream machine and follow the manufacturer's instructions.

Notes: Excellent source of Vitamin C. Good source of Vitamin B2 and Calcium.

Pears in Red Wine

4	pears
3	cups red wine
3/4	cup sugar
1/2	teaspoon cinnamon
1	cup water
2	tablespoons fresh lemon juice

Serves: 4
Prep Time: 0:20

Total Calories 373
Protein 1g
Carbohydrate 66g
Fat 1g
Cholesterol 0mg
Dietary Fiber 4g
% Calories from
Fat 2%

Peel and core the pears. Cover with cold water and add the lemon juice to prevent them from turning brown. In a large saucepan place the red wine, sugar, cinnamon and water. Heat the mixture until the sugar is dissolved. Add the pears and simmer gently for 10-15 minutes until soft, turning them so they are evenly colored by the wine. Remove the pears when soft and place in a serving dish. Bring to the liquid to a boil and reduce by half. Coat the pears with the sauce and serve warm.

Notes: Good source of Vitamin C.

Strawberry Delight

1	package gelatin powder, dissolved in water
1	cup low fat yogurt with fruit
1/2	cup fresh sliced strawberries

Prepare the gelatin according to the instructions. When it begins to set, stir in the yogurt and strawberries. Pour into individual dessert dishes and refrigerate until set. Garnish with fresh strawberries and whipped cream.

Notes: Excellent source of Calcium.

Serves: 4
Prep Time: 0:15
Standing Time:2:00

Total Calories 143
Protein 4g
Carbohydrate 31g
Fat <1g
Cholesterol 3mg
Dietary Fiber <1g
% Calories from
Fat 5%

Fish and Shellfish

Baked Red Snapper

Serving Size: 8
Prep Time: 0:20
Baking Time: 2:00

Total Calories 85
Protein 10g
Carbohydrate 6g
Fat 2g
Cholesterol 18mg
Dietary Fiber 1g
% Calories from
Fat 24%

4	pounds red snapper
1/2	tablespoon olive oil
1/2	tablespoon butter
1	medium chopped onion
3	sticks chopped celery
1	medium chopped green bell pepper
4	cloves crushed garlic
1	teaspoon sugar
1	tablespoon Worcestershire sauce
1/4	cup white wine
8	fluid ounces tomato sauce
1/2	teaspoon Creole seasoning
pinch	salt
pinch	black pepper, fresh ground

Season the fish and place in an ovenproof dish. Melt the olive oil and butter and sauté the onions, celery, green bell pepper and garlic for 5-8 minutes. Add the tomato sauce, Worcestershire sauce and season to taste. Cook slowly for one hour. Heat the oven to 300°F. Pour the wine over the fish and then the sauce. Place in the oven with a small piece of aluminum foil loosely on top. Cook for one hour, basting occasionally. Serve with rice or mashed potatoes as a main dish.

Notes: Excellent source of Vitamin C and B12. Good source of Vitamin B6.

Baked Salmon

1	4-6 pound salmon
1	medium sliced carrot
1	medium sliced onion
4	black peppercorns
1	sprig parsley
1	bay leaf

Serving Size: 4
Prep Time: 0:05
Baking Time: 2:00+

Total Calories 125
Protein 9g
Carbohydrate 16g
Fat 3g
Cholesterol 15mg
Dietary Fiber 5g
% Calories from
Fat 22%

Place the salmon on a large piece of aluminum foil in an ovenproof dish. Slice the carrot and onion and arrange on top of the fish with the peppercorns, parsley and bay leaf. Dab with butter and wrap the foil around the fish. Add the water to the base of the dish and place in a cool oven (250°F) and cook for 2 to 3 hours until cooked through but not dry. Serve hot with Hollandaise Sauce, garnished with lemon wedges. Serve cold, garnished with thinly sliced cucumber, lemon slices and parsley. Cold salmon goes well with mayonnaise or a yogurt dressing.

Notes: Excellent source of Vitamin C, A, B6, B12, Calcium and Iron. Good source of Niacin.

Barbecued Fish with Tarragon Sauce

Serving Size: 4
Prep Time: 0:20

Total Calories 148
Protein 10g
Carbohydrate 9.g
Fat 6g
Cholesterol 28mg
Dietary Fiber <1g
% Calories from
Fat 40%

2	medium red snapper (about 4 pounds)
I	tablespoon fennel
I	tablespoon sage
2	bay leaves
I	tablespoon rosemary
1/2	tablespoon olive oil
I	tablespoon butter
4	tablespoons white wine
pinch	salt
pinch	black pepper

Tarragon Sauce

4	tablespoons tarragon, finely chopped
1/4	cup butter substitute
I	cup lemon juice

Mix the herbs together with the butter and place inside each fish. Brush the fish with oil and place in a wire fish barbecue griller. Grill over hot coals. Combine the ingredients for the tarragon sauce and warm in a small pan. Serve hot as a main dish.

Notes: Excellent source of Vitamin C and B12. Good source of Vitamin A, B6, Calcium and Iron.

Broiled Orange Roughy

2	orange roughy fillets (approx. one pound)
6	medium tomatoes
1	medium red onion chopped
2	cucumbers, peeled and chopped
1	teaspoon salt
2	tablespoons fresh chopped tarragon
1	teaspoon sugar
1/4	cup red wine vinegar
1/2	tablespoon olive oil
1/2	teaspoon ground pepper
2	medium carrots, diced
1/4	cup frozen green peas

Serving Size: 2
Prep Time: 0:20

Total Calories 205
Protein 7g
Carbohydrate 39g
Fat 5g
Cholesterol 10mg
Dietary Fiber 9g
% Calories from
Fat 20%

Remove the core and seeds from the tomatoes and chop coarsely. Combine with the onion, cucumber, tarragon, salt, sugar and chill. Season the orange roughy fillets with salt and fresh ground black pepper and brush (or spray) with olive oil. Broil for 2-3 minutes until cooked. At the same time place the diced carrots in a small saucepan and cover with cold water. Bring to the boil and simmer for 2 minutes. Add the frozen peas and continue to cook for another 2-3 minutes. Drain and set aside. Place the fish on a warm serving dish. Combine the peas and carrots with 1/2 cup of the chilled relish and arrange the vegetable mixture around the fish. Serve the rest of the relish as a side dish. Serve the fish hot with garlic mashed potatoes.

Notes: Excellent source of Vitamin A, C, B6, B1, B2, Folacin and Iron.

Creamy Dijon Sole

Serving Size: 4
Prep Time: 0:15

Total Calories 158
Protein 19g
Carbohydrate 3g
Fat 8g
Cholesterol 0mg
Dietary Fiber 2g
% Calories from
Fat 44%

1	pound dover sole fillets
1	small onion, chopped fine
4	tablespoons nonfat yogurt
2	tablespoons Dijon mustard
2	tablespoons olive oil
1	teaspoon fresh chopped tarragon

Preheat the oven to 425°F. Spray a shallow non-stick ovenproof dish with olive oil spray and arrange the onion slices in the pan. Place the fish over the onion slices. Combine the yogurt, mustard, olive oil and tarragon and season to taste with salt and pepper. Spread over the fish. Bake uncovered for 7-9 minutes. Serve hot with brown rice or small potatoes.

Notes: Good source of Niacin and Calcium.
This dish is relatively high in fat because there is virtually no carbohydrate in white fish. It is a nutritious supper dish, low in calories and delicious.

Ginger-Sesame Salmon

4	salmon steaks (about 2 pounds total wt.)
1	teaspoon fresh lemon juice
1	cup water
2	teaspoons soy sauce
2	teaspoons rice vinegar
1	tablespoon fresh minced ginger root
2	green onions, cut in strips
1	clove crushed garlic
1	tablespoon sesame oil

Serving Size: 4
Prep Time: 0:20

Total Calories 254
Protein 36g
Carbohydrate 6g
Fat 9g
Cholesterol 88mg
Dietary Fiber 2g
% Calories from
Fat 33%

Place the water and fresh lemon juice in a deep non-stick sauté pan or skillet. Bring to a boil. Place the salmon steaks in the water and cover the pan. Reduce the heat and simmer very gently for 6-8 minutes until the fish is opaque in color. Arrange the salmon on a warm serving dish. Mix the soy sauce, rice vinegar and ginger together and spoon over the salmon. Cut the green onions into thin strips and scatter over the top of the fish. In a small pan combine the garlic and sesame oil. Warm the mixture until it browns and drizzle over the top of the fish. Serve hot.

Notes: Excellent source of Vitamin C, B6, B12, B1, Folacin and Niacin. Good source of Vitamin B2, Iron and Zinc.

Grilled Tuna

Serving Size: 4
Prep Time: 0:20

Total Calories 260
Protein 40g
Carbohydrate 1g
Fat 10g
Cholesterol 65mg
Dietary Fiber 0g
% Calories from
Fat 36%

4	medium tuna steaks (about 2 pounds total weight)
1/2	tablespoon olive oil
1/4	teaspoon salt
1/4	teaspoon black pepper, fresh ground

Brush the tuna steaks with olive oil and season with salt and pepper. Place a rack 4" from the broiler and heat for 10 minutes. Broil the steaks 4 minutes on each side. Serve on a bed of brown rice with warm cilantro sauce.

Notes: Excellent source of Vitamin A, B6, B12, B1, B2 and Niacin.

Halibut with Broccoli and Almonds

3/4	pound halibut fillet
2	tablespoons corn starch
1/2	pound broccoli florets
1/2	cup julienned carrots
1/4	cup low-sodium soy sauce
2	teaspoons sesame oil
1	clove garlic
1/2	teaspoon ginger
2	tablespoons almond slivers
2 1/2	cups brown rice

Serving Size: 4
Prep Time: 0:20

Total Calories 590
Protein 30g
Carbohydrate 101g
Fat 8g
Cholesterol 27mg
Dietary Fiber 3g
% Calories from
Fat 12%

Cut halibut into 1" x 2" strips and coat with cornstarch. Combine broccoli, carrots, soy sauce, garlic and ginger in a mixing bowl and set aside. In a large non-stick skillet heat 2 teaspoons of sesame oil, add the fish and fry for 4 to 5 minutes until lightly browned. Remove the fish and set aside. Add the rest of the sesame oil and stir-fry the vegetable mixture for 3 to 4 minutes. Add the almonds and continue to cook for a further minute. Add the fish back to the mixture and warm through for one minute. Serve with the brown rice as a main dish.

Notes: Excellent source of Vitamin C, A, B6, B12, B1, Folacin, Niacin, Iron and Zinc. Good source of Vitamin B2 and Calcium.

Monkfish, Mushrooms and Lentils

2	pounds monkfish
1	tablespoon all-purpose flour,
1	cup lentils
1	medium onion
1	bay leaf
1	leek
2	cloves garlic
2	tablespoons fresh parsley
2	cups mushrooms
1 1/2	cups water
2	teaspoons corn flour
1/2	cup white wine
1	tablespoon olive oil
1	tablespoon butter

Serving Size: 4
Prep Time: 1:00

Total Calories 312
Protein 22g
Carbohydrate 39g
Fat 8g
Cholesterol 18mg
Dietary Fiber 7g
% Calories from
Fat 22%

Place the lentils and bay leaf in a pan with the water. Bring to a boil, cover and simmer for 20-30 minutes until the lentils are cooked. Set aside, still covered. Melt the oil and butter in a wide skillet. Add chopped onion, leek and garlic and sauté for 5 minutes. Add chopped parsley and continue to cook gently for a further 5 minutes. Add the porcine mushrooms and cook for 4-5 minutes more. Stir in the wine and cook for another minute. Add the filleted monkfish, dipped in seasoned flour. Simmer for 4 minutes on each side. Lift the fish out of the skillet and arrange on a large ovenproof dish. Cover and leave in a warm (120°F) oven for 10 minutes. Mix 2 teaspoons of corn flour in 2 tablespoons of water and add to the skillet. Stir over a medium heat until the mixture thickens into a coating sauce. Serve the fish on a bed of lentils, covered with the porcine mushroom sauce.

Notes: Excellent source of Vitamin B6, B1, B2, Folacin, Niacin, Iron and Zinc. Good source of Vitamin C.

Penne with Shrimp

1	tablespoon olive oil
1	medium chopped onion
2	cloves crushed garlic
1/4	cup vegetable broth
28	ounces canned tomatoes, puréed
1/4	pound small shrimp
1/2	pound fresh pasta,
1/2	cup chopped fennel,
1/2	cup fresh chopped mint,
1/4	teaspoon salt
1/4	teaspoon black pepper

Serving Size: 4
Prep Time: 0:30

Total Calories 287
Protein 15g
Carbohydrate 45g
Fat 6g
Cholesterol 85mg
Dietary Fiber 3g
% Calories from
Fat 18%

Heat the oil in a non-stick skillet and sauté the onions, fennel and garlic for 3-5 minutes. Add the stock and the tomatoes and cook for 15 minutes. Cook the pasta separately and drain. Place the shrimp in boiling water and drain after 5 minutes. Mix the shrimp, tomato sauce and fresh mint together and season to taste. Serve hot over the cooked pasta. Garnish with fresh mint.

Notes: Excellent source of Vitamin C, A, B6, B12, B1, B2, Folacin, Niacin and Iron. Good source of Calcium and Zinc.

Salmon and Scallops Brochettes

Serving Size: 6
Prep Time: 0:20

Total Calories 277
Protein 30g
Carbohydrate 25g
Fat 8g
Cholesterol 63mg
Dietary Fiber 1g
% Calories from
Fat 24%

1 1/2	pound salmon
8	medium scallops
16	cherry tomatoes
16	mushrooms
1	tablespoon olive oil
1	tablespoon lemon juice
1	clove crushed garlic
pinch	salt
pinch	black pepper

Cut salmon into 1" cubes. Thread salmon, tomatoes, scallops, mushrooms onto skewers. Brush with mixture of oil, lemon juice, garlic and seasoning. Broil until the fish is cooked, for about 12 to 15 minutes, turning several times. Serve with rice as a main dish.

Notes: Excellent source of Vitamin C, A, B6, B12, B1, B2, Folacin, Niacin and Iron. Good source of Zinc.

Sea Bass with Apples

4	medium sea bass steaks
2	medium red apples
2	sticks chopped celery
2	medium chopped onions
4	teaspoons chopped parsley
I	medium chopped green bell pepper
15	ounces canned tomatoes, drained
1/2	cup vegetable broth
1/4	teaspoon salt
1/4	teaspoon black pepper
pinch	dill

Serving Size: 4
Prep Time: 0:30

Total Calories 233
Protein 27g
Carbohydrate 24g
Fat 4g
Cholesterol 53mg
Dietary Fiber 5g
% Calories from
Fat 14%

Preheat the oven to 350 °F. Place the celery, onions, tomatoes and broth into a pan and cook for 5 minutes. Core and dice the apple and add to the ingredients. Add the parsley and dill and season to taste. Continue cooking a further 2-3 minutes or until completely cooked. Place the mixture in the bottom of an ovenproof dish with the fish steaks on top. Cover with a loose piece of aluminum foil and bake in the oven at 350°F for 10-15 minutes until the fish is white and cooked. Garnish with parsley and lemon wedges. Serve hot with brown rice or mash potato as a main dish.

Notes: Excellent source of Vitamin C, A, B6, B1, Folacin and Niacin. Good source of Calcium, Iron and Zinc.

Seafood Crepes (Part 1 of 3)

Serving Size: 6
Prep Time: 1:30

Total Calories 159
Protein 9g
Carbohydrate 24g
Fat 3
Cholesterol 75mg
Dietary Fiber 3g
% Calories from
Fat 18%

1	cup wild rice, cooked
1	teaspoon chopped shallots
1	teaspoon crushed garlic
2	eggs
2	egg whites
1 1/2	cups skim milk
3/4	cup whole-grain wheat flour
1/4	cup white flour
2	teaspoons whipped butter

Blend all ingredients together for one minute until the consistency of cream. Cover and chill in refrigerator for 4 hours. Place a 6" non-stick crepe or omelette pan on medium heat, brush with olive oil spray and add 1 1/2 ounces of the batter in the center when hot. Turn quickly in all directions to cover the bottom of the pan. After 30 seconds, turn the crepe and cook on the other side for 15 seconds. Remove the crepe and set on one side. Re-oil the pan in between cooking the rest of the crepes.

Notes: Excellent source of Vitamin B2. Good source of
Vitamin B1, Folacin, Niacin and Zinc.

Roasted Tomato Sauce (for Seafood Crepes) (Part 2 of 3)

5	tomatoes, red ripe
12	cloves garlic
1	bunch green onions
3	tablespoons fresh basil
1	tablespoon fresh oregano
1/2	teaspoon black pepper
1/4	teaspoon salt
pinch	crushed red chili peppers,

Sear tomatoes in a hot, non-stick skillet until charred. Remove tomatoes, chop coarsely and place with all of the other ingredients in the pan. Simmer 45 minutes to an hour.

Notes: Excellent source of Vitamin C. Good source of Vitamin A, B6 and Folacin.

Serving Size: 6
Prep Time: 0:05
Pre-cooking
Stand Time:4:00+

Total Calories 40
Protein 2g
Carbohydrate 9g
Fat <1g
Cholesterol 0mg
Dietary Fiber 2g
% Calories from
Fat 9%

Seafood Crepes Filling (Part 3 of 3)

Serving Size: 6
Prep Time: 1:00

Total Calories 202
Protein 28g
Carbohydrate 8g
Fat 6g
Cholesterol 71mg
Dietary Fiber 2g
% Calories from
Fat 37%

1/2	pound halibut fillet
1/4	pound shrimp
1/4	pound crabmeat
1	tablespoon shallots
1	teaspoon crushed garlic
1	tablespoon diced onion
1	tablespoon chopped tarragon
1	tablespoon chives
6	ounces watercress
3	egg whites
pinch	nutmeg
1/4	teaspoon white pepper
1/4	pinch salt
3	ounces mozzarella cheese, part skim milk

Preheat oven to 300°F. Place halibut, shrimp and crab meat together with shallots, garlic, onion, herbs, spices and seasoning into a blender. Add egg whites and chop coarsely, using the pulse setting control. Steam the kale and watercress for 1-2 minutes and add to the seafood mixture. Oil a glass baking dish and add the mixture to it and bake for 20 minutes. Remove from the oven and chop lightly. Mix with the mozzarella cheese and fill crepes . Place in a baking dish, cover and bake at 325°F for 20-30 minutes until cooked through. Remove and place each crepe on a plate and top with Roasted Tomato Sauce . Serve with a green salad as a main dish.

Notes: Excellent source of Vitamin C, A, B6, B12, B2, Folacin, Niacin and Calcium. Good source of Vitamin B1, Iron and Zinc.

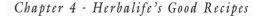

Shrimp in Black Bean Sauce

1	can black beans, drained
1/2	tablespoon olive oil
2	tablespoons fresh minced ginger root
4	cloves crushed garlic
1 1/2	pounds shrimp
2	tablespoons corn starch
2	tablespoons soy sauce
4	chopped scallions
2	cups cooked rice

Serving Size: 6
Prep Time: 0:15

Total Calories 486
Protein 35g
Carbohydrate 75g
Fat 4g
Cholesterol 173mg
Dietary Fiber 6g
% Calories from
Fat 7%

Heat the oil in a heavy, non-stick skillet and cook the ginger and garlic for one minute. Add the partially mashed beans, the shrimp and 1/2 cup of water. Cover and cook for 3 minutes or until shrimp is cooked. Mix the corn starch with 2 tablespoons of water and add to the pan. Mix well until the sauce thickens – about 1 to 2 minutes. Add the soy sauce and warm through. Sprinkle with the scallions and serve with the rice.

Notes: Excellent source of Vitamin B12, Folacin, Niacin, Iron and Zinc. Good source of Vitamin B6 and Calcium.

Sizzling Swordfish, Broccoli and Peanuts

Serving Size: 4
Prep Time: 0:20

Total Calories 314
Protein 23g
Carbohydrate 38g
Fat 7g
Cholesterol 33mg
Dietary Fiber 3g
% Calories from
Fat 22%

3/4	pound swordfish
2	tablespoons corn flour
1/2	pound broccoli florets
1/2	cup julienned carrots
1/4	cup low-sodium soy sauce
1/2	teaspoon sesame oil
1	clove garlic
1	teaspoon ground ginger
1	teaspoon peanut oil
1	tablespoon unsalted peanuts
2 1/2	cups cooked brown rice

Combine the swordfish, cut into 1" X 2" strips with the corn starch and cover evenly. In another bowl, combine the vegetables, sesame oil and seasoning. Heat 2 teaspoons of the peanut oil in a large skillet and add the fish, cooking until lightly browned (4-5 minutes). Remove the fish and set aside. Heat the remaining teaspoon of peanut oil and stir-fry vegetable mixture and peanuts. Cook for 4 minutes. Place the fish in the mixture and cook covered for another minute. Serve over cooked brown rice.

Notes: Excellent source of Vitamin C, A, B6, B12, Folacin and Niacin. Good source of V i t a m i n B1, B2, Iron and Zinc.

Teriyaki Salmon

2	pounds salmon
1	tablespoon packed brown sugar
1/4	cup soy sauce
1	tablespoon olive oil
1	teaspoon all-purpose flour
1/2	cup white wine
1	teaspoon mustard
6	slices pineapple

Serving Size: 8
Prep Time: 0:45

Total Calories 618
Protein 9g
Carbohydrate 146g
Fat 6g
Cholesterol 11mg
Dietary Fiber 2g
% Calories from
Fat 8%

Combine soy sauce, brown sugar, olive oil, flour, wine and mustard in a small pan. Bring to a boil, then simmer for 3 minutes. Set aside to cool. Wipe fish and pat dry. Preheat the oven to 320°F. Place the fish in the marinade and refrigerate for 15 minutes. Remove the fish from the refrigerator and place on a non-stick oiled pan. Place a slice of pineapple on each fillet. Heat the marinade and brush the fish with hot marinade. Place in the oven for 15 to 20 minutes until white and cooked. Remove and serve garnished with tomatoes for color. Serve with rice as a main dish.

Notes: Excellent source of Vitamin C, B6, B12, B1, B2, Folacin, Niacin and Iron.

Trout with Almonds

Serving Size: 4
Prep Time: 0:30

Total Calories 268
Protein 21g
Carbohydrate 11g
Fat 12g
Cholesterol 65mg
Dietary Fiber <1g
% Calories from
Fat 47%

4	trout
1/4	cup almond slivers
1/4	cup flour
1/2	tablespoon butter
1/2	tablespoon olive oil
1	lemon
1/4	teaspoon salt
1/4	teaspoon black pepper

Roll each prepared trout in the seasoned flour. Heat the oil and butter in a large non-stick skillet. Fry the trout 3-4 minutes on each side. Lift from the pan and set aside in a warm place. Add the almonds to the pan, adding extra oil and butter only if absolutely necessary. When browned, lift from the heat and set aside with the fish. Remove the skillet from the heat and add the lemon juice. Mix well and spoon the almonds and juices over the fish. Serve hot as a main dish.

Notes: Excellent source of Vitamin C, B12, B1 and B2. Good source of Iron.

White Fish with Ginger and Lemon

4	medium halibut steaks (about 2 pounds)
2	tablespoons olive oil
2	garlic cloves
3	cups frozen green peas
2	sliced scallions
1	teaspoon peeled and chopped ginger root
1	tablespoon grated lemon peel
1	cup lemon juice
2	cups cooked brown rice

Serving Size: 4
Prep Time: 0:20

Total Calories 460
Protein 44g
Carbohydrate 45g
Fat 11g
Cholesterol 54mg
Dietary Fiber 6g
% Calories from
Fat 23%

Heat one tablespoon of the olive oil in a large nonstick skillet. Sauté the fish steaks until they turn white. Remove the fish and set aside in a warm place. Add the rest of the oil, peas, scallions, ginger and lemon peel. Cook, stirring frequently until the peas are cooked. Return the fish to the pan and heat thoroughly. Serve on a bed of brown rice. Garnish with lemon wedges and parsley. Serve as a main dish.

Notes: Excellent source of Vitamin C, A, B6, B12, B1, Folacin, Niacin and Iron. Good source of Vitamin B2, Calcium and Zinc.

Meat

Beef and Vegetable Stew

1 1/2	pounds lean beef, cut in pieces
2	cups beef broth
2	medium onions, cut in quarters
1	bay leaf
1	teaspoon thyme
1/2	teaspoon oregano
1/2	teaspoon marjoram
1/2	teaspoon black pepper, fresh ground
4	medium sliced carrots
1	cup frozen peas
2	tablespoons fresh chopped parsley
1/2	teaspoon salt
2	cloves crushed garlic

Serving Size: 6
Prep Time: 0:10
Baking Time: 2:00+

Total Calories 157
Protein 19g
Carbohydrate 12g
Fat 4g
Cholesterol 34 mg
Dietary Fiber 4g
% Calories from
Fat 22%

Place the flour and salt in a large bag and add the beef so it is coated. Remove from the bag. Heat the oil in a large casserole dish and brown a few cubes of beef. Set aside and brown some more until all are done. Add the onion, cover the dish and saute for 3-4 minutes. Add the beef broth, bay leaf, thyme, oregano, marjoram and simmer in the covered dish for 1 1/2 hours. Add the carrot and simmer for another 30 minutes. Add the peas and seasoning to taste. Serve hot.

Notes: Excellent source of Vitamin A, B6, B12, Folacin, Niacin and Zinc. Good source of Vitamin C, B1, B2 and Iron.

Beef Bourguignon

Serving Size: 8
Prep Time: 0:10
Baking Time: 2:00+

Total Calories 237
Protein 28g
Carbohydrate 10g
Fat 6g
Cholesterol 66mg
Dietary fiber 2 g
% Calories from
Fat 25%

2	pounds lean beef, cubed in 1" pieces
5	medium sliced onions
1	cup beef broth
1	leek, sliced 1/4" thick
1	carrot, sliced 1/4" thick
1	cup red wine
1/2	tablespoon olive oil
1	teaspoon fresh thyme
1	teaspoon fresh marjoram
1/2	teaspoon fresh ground black pepper
1/2	pound sliced mushrooms
1	tablespoon flour

Preheat oven to 300°F. Heat olive oil in a heavy non-stick skillet. Sauté onions and remove. Place beef cubes in a plastic bag with seasoned flour and brown in the pan. Remove and place in a casserole dish. Add the vegetables to the skillet and stir fry for 3-4 minutes. Transfer to the casserole dish and add the wine and broth. Cover and cook in a slow oven for 1 1/2 to 2 hours. Serve with rice or mashed potatoes.

Notes: Excellent source of Vitamin B6, B12, B2, Folacin, Niacin, Iron and Zinc. Good source of Vitamin B1.

Herb Pork Roast

5	pounds pork loin
3	tablespoons fresh rosemary
10	cloves garlic
1	teaspoon salt
1	tablespoon black pepper, fresh ground
1	tablespoon fresh thyme
1	tablespoon olive oil
2	sprigs fresh rosemary
2	sprigs fresh thyme

Serving Size: 6
Prep Time: 0:10
Baking Time: 2:00

Total Calories 320
Protein 30g
Carbohydrate 4g
Fat 20g
Cholesterol 93mg
Dietary Fiber <1g
% Calories from
Fat 57%

Place the fresh rosemary and thyme, black pepper, salt and olive oil in a blender and add the garlic. Place the mixture into small incisions made in the pork loin. Tie 2 fresh sprigs each of rosemary and thyme across the top of the loin. Allow to stand for 2 hours. Preheat the oven to 350°F. Roast for 1 1/2 to 2 hours until the skewer comes out clear. Allow to stand for 20 minutes before slicing.

Notes: Excellent source of Vitamin B6, B12, B1, B2, Niacin, Iron and Zinc.

Lamb Kebabs

Serving Size: 4
Prep Time: 0:30

Total Calories 119
Protein 13g
Carbohydrate 11g
Fat 3g
Cholesterol 37mg
Dietary Fiber 2g
% Calories from
Fat 24%

1/2	pound cubed lamb
1/2	cup lemon juice
1/4	cup white wine vinegar
1	clove crushed garlic
1/2	teaspoon salt
1/2	teaspoon fresh ground black pepper
2	tomatoes
1	medium onion
1	bell pepper
6	mushrooms

Combine the lemon juice, white wine vinegar, garlic, salt and black pepper. Place the cubes of lamb in it and marinate for at least 2 hours (or overnight). Place the lamb cubes on a skewer, alternating with onion quarters, whole mushrooms, green pepper slices and tomatoes. Broil for 6-8 minutes, turning several times. Serve over rice, couscous or with pita bread. This dish goes well with a lemon-yogurt or cucumber-yogurt sauce.

Notes: Excellent source of Vitamin C, B12, Folacin, Niacin and Zinc. Good source of Vitamin A, B6, B1, B2 and Iron.

Meatballs

3/4	pound ground extra lean lamb
3/4	cup cooked rice
1	medium chopped onion
2	tablespoons finely chopped parsley
1	teaspoon fresh thyme
1/2	teaspoon marjoram
1/4	teaspoon salt
1/4	teaspoon black pepper
2	egg whites
1	teaspoon extra virgin olive oil
1/2	cup flour

Serving Size: 4
Prep Time: 0:30

Total Calories 334
Protein 18g
Carbohydrate 42g
Fat 9g
Cholesterol 46mg
Dietary Fiber 1g
% Calories from
Fat 25%

Preheat the oven to 200°F. Combine the rice, onion, parsley, thyme, marjoram and lightly beaten egg whites together in a large bowl. Add the ground lamb and mix evenly. Form 2" sized meat balls and roll them in the flour. Heat a large non-stick skillet and lightly spray with olive oil. Brown the meatballs on a medium high heat and then place them in an ovenproof dish. Cook for 20 minutes and serve hot with a tomato or brown sauce. Serve garnished with parsley.

Notes: Excellent source of Vitamin B1, Niacin, Iron and Zinc. Good source of Vitamin B6, B12, B2 and Folacin.

This recipe can also be made ground lean beef, veal or turkey.

Oriental Beef

Serving Size: 4
Baking time: 0:20
Maritinetime:2:00+

Total Calories 214
Protein 29g
Carbohydrate 5g
Fat 5g
Cholesterol 66mg
Dietary Fiber 2g
% Calories from
Fat 25%

1	pound lean beef, cut in pieces
1/2	cup soy sauce, Tamari
1/2	cup red wine
4	finely chopped scallions
4	cloves crushed garlic
1	teaspoon black pepper, fresh ground
1/4	teaspoon coriander
1	teaspoon minced ginger root
1	teaspoon brown sugar

Combine soy sauce, red wine, scallions, garlic, black pepper and salt together in a shallow ovenproof dish. Put the beef in the marinade and leave for at least 2 hours (or overnight). Remove from the marinade and broil or barbecue for 5-10 minutes until cooked.

Notes: Excellent source of Vitamin B6, B12, Niacin and Zinc.
        Good source of Vitamin B1, B2 and Iron.

Rack of Lamb with Herbs

2 1/2	pounds lamb cutlets
2	cloves garlic, peeled and sliced
2	tablespoons fresh herbs
1	teaspoon sea salt
1/4	teaspoon black pepper, fresh ground

Serving Size: 4
Prep Time: 0:10
Baking Time 0:20+

Total Calories 99
Protein 15g
Carbohydrate <1g
Fat 4g
Cholesterol 42mg
Dietary Fiber <1g
% Calories from
Fat 35%

Preheat the oven to 450°F. Remove excess fat from the lamb. With a knife make small incisions into the lamb and insert slices of garlic to infuse flavor. Combine the fresh herbs (oregano, thyme, marjoram and sage are good) and rub onto the lamb. Place the rack on a roasting pan with the fat side up. Place in the oven and immediately reduce the heat to 400°F. Bake for 20-25 minutes depending on how well done desired. Remove from the oven, loosely cover with aluminum foil and allow the meat to rest before serving. The butcher can arrange the cutlets in a circle like a crown and partially cut the ribs through. Paper covers may also be placed on the ends of each rib as a garnish before serving.

Notes: Excellent source of Vitamin B12, Niacin and Zinc.
Good source of Vitamin B2 and Iron.

Trim the meat of all visible fat to reduce the fat content.

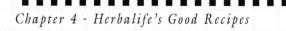

Shepherd's Pie

1	pound lamb shank, ground
2	medium chopped onion
1	clove crushed garlic
1/2	teaspoon fresh thyme, chopped fine
1/2	teaspoon fresh oregano, chopped fine
1	tablespoon Worcestershire sauce
1	tablespoon ketchup
3/4	cup chicken broth
1/2	cup tomato purée
1/2	teaspoon salt
1/2	teaspoon white pepper
2	pounds potatoes, peeled and sliced
1/2	cup skim milk

Serving Size: 4
Prep Time: 0:15
Baking Time:0:45

Total Calories 288
Protein 23g
Carbohydrate 20g
Fat 13g
Cholesterol 62mg
Dietary Fiber 3g
% Calories from
Fat 40%

Preheat the oven to 375°F. Cut the potatoes into even-sized pieces and cover with cold water. Season with half of the salt and bring to a boil. Simmer for 10-12 minutes until the potatoes are soft. Drain and mash with the milk. Set aside. Heat a skillet and spray with olive oil. Sauté the onion and garlic until transparent. Add the ground meat and brown quickly. Add the thyme, oregano, Worcestershire sauce, ketchup and tomato paste. Place the meat mixture in the base of an ovenproof dish. Cover with the mashed potatoes. Use a fork to decorate the top. Bake in the center of the oven for 45 minutes. Serve hot.

Notes: Excellent source of Vitamin C, B6, B12, B1, B2, Folacin, Niacin, Iron and Zinc. Good source of Vitamin A.

This can be made with beef - called Cottage Pie in England.

Sloppy Joe's

3/4	pound extra lean ground beef
1	cup bread crumbs
1	green bell pepper
1	tablespoon red wine vinegar
1	tablespoon dry mustard
14	fluid ounces ketchup
1	teaspoon chili powder

Serving Size: 4
Prep Time: 0:45

Total Calories 466
Protein 25g
Carbohydrate 69g
Fat 9g
Cholesterol 43mg
Dietary Fiber 6g
% Calories from Fat
17%

Preheat the oven to 300°F. Combine the ingredients together in a large bowl. Transfer to an oiled ovenproof dish and bake slowly for 40 minutes. Serve with hamburger buns.

Notes: Excellent source of Vitamin C, A, B6, B12, B1, B2, Niacin, Iron and Zinc. Good source of Folacin.

Sun-Dried Tomato Meatloaf

Serving Size: 6
Prep Time: 0:10
Baking Time: 1:00

Total Calories 310
Protein 21g
Carbohydrate 32g
Fat 10g
Cholesterol 39mg
Dietary Fiber 3g
% Calories from
Fat 30%

1	pound extra lean ground beef
1	medium onion
2	cloves garlic
1/2	cup sun-dried tomatoes, soaked
1/2	pound sliced mushrooms
1	egg white
2	cups bread crumbs
1/2	teaspoon fresh oregano
1/2	teaspoon fresh thyme
1/4	teaspoon salt
1/4	teaspoon black pepper, fresh ground

Preheat the oven to 350°F. Heat a large skillet and spray with olive oil. Sauté the onion and garlic until transparent for 3-4 minutes. Drain and chop the tomatoes. In a large bowl combine the meat, egg white, bread crumbs, tomatoes and mushrooms. Add the sautéed vegetables and transfer to an oiled loaf pan. Cover with a loose piece of foil and bake for an hour. Let it cool for 15 minutes before removing from the pan and slicing. Serve hot or cold.

Notes: Excellent source of Vitamin B12, B1, B2, Niacin, Iron and Zinc. Good source of Vitamin B6 and Folacin.

To reduce fat, select beef shank and have the butcher grind it for you. This may also be made with veal, lamb or turkey.

Veal Cutlets with Tarragon

4	veal cutlets 3/4" thick
3	sprigs fresh tarragon, finely chopped
1/4	teaspoon black pepper, fresh ground
1/2	cup chicken broth

Serving Size: 4
Prep Time: 0:20

Total Calories 263
Protein 48g
Carbohydrate 1g
Fat 6g
Cholesterol 191mg
Dietary Fiber <1g
% Calories from
Fat 21%

Combine the tarragon with the black pepper and rub over the chops. Heat a large non-stick skillet. Add the chops and cook for 3-4 minutes on each side over a medium heat. Remove and keep in a warm place on a serving dish. Add the chicken broth to the skillet and stir the browned drippings into the broth. Add the remaining tarragon leaves and reduce the sauce by half by cooking for 3-4 minutes. Adjust the seasoning and spoon the sauce over the cutlets. Garnish with additional fresh tarragon leaves.

Notes: Excellent source of Vitamin B6, B12, B2, Niacin and Zinc. Good source of Vitamin B1, Folacin and Iron.

One teaspoon of crumbled dry tarragon may be used if fresh is not available.

Veal Scallopini

Serving Size: 6
Prep Time: 0:30

Total Calories 89
Protein 12g
Carbohydrate 1g
Fat 2g
Cholesterol 33mg
Dietary Fiber <1g
% Calories from
Fat 22%

1 1/2   pounds veal sirloin, cut in 6 pieces
1   teaspoon olive oil
1   cup sliced mushrooms
1/2   cup Marsala wine
1/2   teaspoon salt
1/2   teaspoon white pepper
1   clove crushed garlic
1/2   teaspoon oregano

Pound the veal to thin slices. Heat the olive oil in a large non-stick skillet and quickly brown the slices one at a time for 1-2 minutes. Set the pieces to one side in a warm place. Add the rest of the ingredients to the skillet and heat. Replace the veal, reduce the heat and simmer for 12-15 minutes until the veal is tender. Serve with mashed potato or pasta.

Notes: Excellent source of Vitamin B12 and Niacin. Good source of Vitamin B6, B2 and Zinc.

Veal Stew

6	slices veal shank, approx. 2 pounds total weight
16	ounces canned tomatoes
12	baby carrots
4	small new potatoes
1	stick julienned celery
1/2	cup chopped onions
1	cup sliced mushrooms
1	julienned leek
1	sprig thyme
1	sprig rosemary
5	leaves fresh basil
1	bay leaf
1	clove crushed garlic
1	cup white wine
1/2	teaspoon salt
1/4	teaspoon black pepper, fresh ground

Serving Size: 6
Prep Time: 0:15
Cooking Time: 2:00

Total Calories 399
Protein 51g
Carbohydrate 24g
Fat 7g
Cholesterol 177mg
Dietary Fiber 3g
% Calories from
Fat 18%

Place all the ingredients in a large stew pan. Cover and simmer for 3 hours over gentle heat – the water should bubble very little. Adjust liquid by adding water during cooking time. Serve hot.

Notes: Excellent source of Vitamin C, B6, B12, B1, B2, Folacin, Niacin, Iron and Zinc. Good source of Vitamin A.

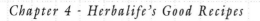

Serving Size: 4
Prep Time: 0:25

Total Calories 189
Protein 22g
Carbohydrate 2g
Fat 8g
Cholesterol 104mg
Dietary Fiber <1g
% Calories from
Fat 42%

Veal with Green Peppercorns

1 1/2	pound veal blade portion
3	tablespoons green peppercorns
1	tablespoon chopped scallions
1/2	cup red wine
1/2	tablespoon olive oil

Crush the peppercorns and rub into the veal cutlets. Heat the oil in a large non-stick skillet and brown the cutlets for 18-20 minutes. Remove the cutlets and add the scallions and wine. Allow to boil and reduce a little. Return the veal to the pan and serve hot, coated with the sauce.

Notes: Excellent source of Niacin and Zinc. Good source of Vitamin B2.

Pasta and Rice

Brown Rice Pilaf

Serving Size: 6
Prep Time: 1:15

Total Calories 188
Protein 5g
Carbohydrate 33g
Fat 4g
Cholesterol 1mg
Dietary Fiber 2g
% Calories from
Fat 20%

3/4	cup brown rice
2	cups vegetable broth
1	package frozen peas 16 ounce
1	chopped red bell pepper
1	medium chopped onion
3	cloves garlic, crushed
1	tablespoon olive oil

Heat the oil in a non-stick skillet. Sauté onions and garlic for 3-5 minutes. Add the brown rice and vegetable broth. Bring to a boil and boil for 5 minutes. Turn down the heat, cover the pan and simmer for 40 minutes. Check the level of liquid occasionally and add extra if necessary. Boil the peas and chopped peppers for 3 minutes and add the rice mixture. Mix thoroughly. Goes well with chicken or a bean dish.

Notes: Excellent source of Vitamin C, A, B6, B1, Folacin and Iron. Good source of Vitamin B2, Niacin and Zinc.

Optional extra. Add 1 cup diced chicken.

Lemon Rice

1 1/2	cups long-grain rice
1 1/2	cups water
2	tablespoons fresh lemon juice
1	tablespoon olive oil
1	tablespoon fresh parsley
1	medium onion, chopped fine
1/4	teaspoon fresh dill

Serving Size: 4
Prep Time: 0:30

Total Calories 224
Protein 1g
Carbohydrate 48g
Fat 3g
Cholesterol 0mg
Dietary Fiber <1g
% Calories from
Fat 14%

Heat a non-stick skillet and spray with olive oil. Sauté the onion for 2-3 minutes until transparent. Add the rice and dill. Cover with the water. Simmer covered for 20-30 minutes until cooked. Add the fresh lemon juice and season to taste. Serve garnished with parsley.

Linguini with Clam Sauce

4	cans clams, canned
1	large chopped onion
6	cloves crushed garlic
6	tablespoons chopped fresh parsley
1/4	cup extra virgin olive oil
1/2	teaspoon black pepper, fresh ground
1	lb linguini

Serving Size: 6
Prep Time: 1:00

Total Calories 531
Protein 38g
Carbohydrate 65g
Fat 12g
Cholesterol 71mg
Dietary Fiber 2g
% Calories from
Fat 21%

Heat the oil in a heavy skillet. Sauté the onion and garlic for 3-4 minutes until translucent. Add half the clam juice drained from the cans and simmer for 30 minutes. Add the rest of the clam juice, the clams, parsley and pepper. Simmer for 5 minutes. In a large pan of salted water boil the linguini for 5-7 minutes, or until cooked. Serve in a pasta bowl topped with the clam mixture and freshly ground Parmesan cheese.

Notes: Excellent source of Vitamin C, B12, B1, Folacin, Niacin, Iron and Zinc. Good source of Vitamin A, B6 and Calcium.

Macaroni and Cheese

4	ounces macaroni
2	quarts water
I	teaspoon salt
I	tablespoon butter
I	tablespoon flour
I	cup skim milk
I	cup lowfat cheddar cheese
1/8	teaspoon cayenne pepper
I	tablespoon grated Parmesan cheese

Serving Size: 4
Prep Time: 0:10
Baking Time: 0:40

Total Calories 240
Protein 13g
Carbohydrate 26g
Fat 6g
Cholesterol 16mg
Dietary Fiber <1g
% Calories from
Fat 25%

Preheat the oven to 350°F. Boil the water and salt and add the macaroni. Cook for 5-7 minutes until tender. While the macaroni is cooking, melt the butter in a medium saucepan and add the flour. Stirring over gentle heat, make a roux so that the mixture pulls away from the sides. Add the milk and mix to a smooth-pouring consistency. Add the macaroni, seasonings and 2/3 of the cheddar cheese. Continue to stir until the cheese melts. Turn the mixture into a greased ovenproof dish and top with the remaining cheddar cheese and Parmesan. Place in the oven and melt the cheese on the top so it is a rich brown color. Serve hot as a main dish.

Notes: Excellent source of Vitamin B12, B1, B2 and Calcium.
Good source of Niacin and Zinc.

Noodles with Tuna

Serving Size: 6
Prep Time: 0:45

Total Calories 322
Protein 14g
Carbohydrate 43g
Fat 10g
Cholesterol 8mg
Dietary Fiber 1g
% Calories from
Fat 28%

1	6 ounce can tuna in water
1	tablespoon fresh lemon juice
3/4	pound linguini
4	quarts water
1/4	teaspoon salt
1/4	teaspoon black pepper, fresh ground
1	tablespoon extra virgin olive oil

Cook the pasta for 8-9 minutes until tender. Drain well and lay in a warm serving dish. While the pasta is cooking, prepare the tuna sauce. Drain the tuna and mix with the lemon juice and olive oil. Season to taste and set on top of the linguini. Sprinkle a little grated Parmesan or Romano cheese on the top.

Notes: Excellent source of Vitamin B12, B1 and Niacin. Good source of Vitamin B2 and Iron.

Paella

1	pound boneless chicken breasts without skin
1	pound long-grain brown rice
4	large tomatoes, peeled and chopped
1	medium red bell pepper, seeded and chopped
1	medium green bell pepper, seeded and chopped
1	16 ounce package frozen green peas
1	medium chopped onion
1	10 oz can artichoke hearts, drained
3	sprigs fresh parsley
1	bay leaf
1	sprig marjoram
2	tablespoons extra virgin olive oil
1/2	teaspoon salt
1/2	teaspoon pepper
1/2	teaspoon saffron
1/2	pound mushrooms, sliced
3	cups chicken bouillon

Serving Size: 6
Prep Time: 1:15

Total Calories 444
Protein 23g
Carbohydrate 70g
Fat 8g
Cholesterol 36mg
Dietary Fiber 6g
% Calories from
Fat 16%

Cut the chicken breasts into bite size pieces and place in a medium saucepan. Cover with half of the chicken bouillon and the water and simmer gently for 10-15 minutes or until tender. Remove the chicken and keep covered in a warm place. Retain the broth. Heat the olive oil in a large non-stick skillet or paella dish. Sauté the garlic and onions for 3-4 minutes until transparent. Stir in the rice and the rest of the chicken broth, salt, pepper and saffron. Bring to a boil, stirring constantly. Reduce the heat, cover the pan and simmer for 30 minutes.

Add the broth and set aside from cooking the chicken if needed to keep the mixture moist. Remove the bay leaf. Add the chicken pieces and frozen peas and cook for another 5 minutes over low heat. Add the artichoke hearts and other optional extras at this stage. Continue to heat through for 3-4 minutes. Serve in a paella dish (a large flat dish or copper pan) and garnish with strips of peppers and sprigs of parsley.

Notes: Excellent source of Vitamin C, A, B6, B1, B2, Folacin, Niacin, Calcium, Iron and Zinc.

Optional Extras: 1 dozen mussels, 1/2 cup prawns, 1/2 cup of lobster and/or 4 ounces of chorizo (paprika sausage).

Pasta and Eggplant

2	tablespoons olive oil
1	eggplant, peeled and chopped
4	cloves crushed garlic
28	ounces canned tomatoes
1/4	teaspoon hot chili peppers
1/2	teaspoon salt
1/2	teaspoon black pepper
2	tablespoons fresh chopped parsley
1	tablespoon grated parmesan cheese

Serving Size: 4
Prep Time: 0:30

Total Calories 434
Protein 17g
Carbohydrate 79g
Fat 7g
Cholesterol 84mg
Dietary Fiber 5g
% Calories from
Fat 14%

Cook the pasta by boiling in salted water until tender. Meanwhile, heat one tablespoon of the oil in a large non-stick skillet and sauté the onion and garlic for 3-5 minutes. Add half of the eggplant and cook for 8-10 minutes until tender. Remove and keep warm. Heat the rest of the olive oil and cook the remainder of the eggplant. Add the tomatoes, chili peppers and seasoning. Return the eggplant to the pan and warm the whole mixture. Drain the pasta and serve with the sauce on top. Garnish with fresh parsley. Serve the Parmesan cheese separately.

Notes: Excellent source of Vitamin C, A, B6, B1, B2, Folacin, Niacin and Iron. Good source of Calcium and Zinc.

Serving Size: 6
Prep Time: 0:40

Total Calories 296
Protein 12g
Carbohydrate 55g
Fat 3g
Cholesterol 0mg
Dietary Fiber 6g
% Calories from
Fat 9%

Pasta Primavera

1	pound pea pods or mangetout
1	pound asparagus
1	cup green beans sliced in 2" lengths
1/2	cup carrots sliced thin
1	tablespoon olive oil
1/2	cup diced red bell pepper
1/2	cup diced yellow bell pepper
2	tablespoons chopped chives
4	tablespoons chopped fresh parsley
3/4	pound angel hair pasta

Bring a large pot of salted water to the boil. Blanch the pea pods, asparagus, green beans and carrots separately by dipping for 30 seconds and placing in ice cold water immediately afterwards for 30 seconds. Drain and pat dry. Save the cooking water. Heat the olive oil in a large skillet and sauté the bell peppers. Add the blanched vegetables and continue to heat for another 1-2 minutes. Reboil the water and cook the pasta for 3-4 minutes, drain and transfer to a warm serving bowl. Add the hot vegetables and chives, toss and season to taste. Serve the pasta on individual pasta dishes and pass fresh grated Parmesan cheese for topping.

Notes: Excellent source of Vitamin C, A, B6, B1, B2, Folacin, Niacin and Iron. Good source of Zinc.

Penne with Shrimp

1	tablespoon olive oil
1	medium chopped onion
2	cloves crushed garlic
1/4	cup vegetable broth
28	ounces tomatoes, canned puréed
1/4	pound small shrimp
1/2	pound fresh pasta
1/2	cup chopped fennel
1/2	cup fresh chopped mint
1/4	teaspoon salt
1/4	teaspoon black pepper, fresh ground

Serving Size: 4
Prep Time: 0:30

Total Calories 287
Protein 15g
Carbohydrate 45g
Dietary Fiber 3g
Cholesterol 85mg
Dietary Fiber 3g
% Calories from
Fat 18%

Heat the oil in a non-stick skillet and sauté the onions, fennel and garlic for 3-5 minutes. Add the stock and the tomatoes and cook for 15 minutes. Cook the pasta separately and drain. Place the shrimp in boiling water and drain after 5 minutes. Mix the shrimp, tomato sauce and fresh mint together and season to taste. Serve hot over the cooked pasta. Garnish with fresh mint.

Notes: Excellent source of Vitamin C, A, B6, B12, B1, B2, Folacin, Niacin and Iron. Good source of Calcium and Zinc.

Serving Size: 4
Prep Time: 1:00

Total Calories 218
Protein 7g
Carbohydrate 34g
Fat 6g
Cholesterol 0mg
Dietary Fiber 4g
% Calories from
Fat 25%

Quinoa-Nut Vegetable Pilaf

1	cup quinoa, rinsed and drained
1	tablespoon olive oil
1	medium chopped onion
1	clove crushed garlic
1	medium diced carrot
2	tablespoons almonds, toasted and chopped
2	tablespoons fresh chopped parsley

Rinse the quinoa under cold running water for 4-5 minutes to remove the grit and bitter flavorings. Heat the olive oil in a large, non-stick pan and sauté the onion and garlic for 3-5 minutes until transparent. Add the carrot and continue to cook in the covered pan for 2-3 minutes more. Add the quinoa, water and salt and boil for 2 minutes. Reduce the heat, cover the pot and simmer for 20 minutes until tender. Add the chopped, toasted almonds and mix well. Add additional water if necessary so that the pilaf is moist. Serve hot.

Notes: Excellent source of Vitamin A and Iron. Good source of Vitamin B6, B1, B2, Folacin and Zinc.

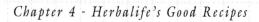

Risotto

1	cup rice
1 3/4	cups vegetable broth
1/2	medium chopped onion
1/2	tablespoon extra virgin olive oil
1	teaspoon white wine

Serving Size: 4
Prep Time: 0:40

Total Calories 260
Protein 6g
Carbohydrate 49g
Fat 4g
Cholesterol 1mg
Dietary Fiber 2g
% Calories from
Fat 13%

Heat the oil in a non-stick pan and sauté the onion and garlic for 3-4 minutes until transparent. Add the rice and vegetable broth and bring to a boil. Boil for a minute, then reduce the heat, cover the pan and simmer for 25 minutes or until tender. Add extra water if necessary. Serve hot.

Notes: Excellent source of Vitamin A and B12. Good source of Niacin, Iron and Zinc.

Optional Extras: 1/2 teaspoon of powdered saffron or 1/2 cup of porcine mushrooms (sliced and sautéed with the onions and garlic).

Spaghetti with Artichoke Hearts

Serving Size: 4
Prep Time: 0:30

Total Calories 355
Protein 14g
Carbohydrate 56g
Fat 9g
Cholesterol 4mg
Dietary Fiber 7g
% Calories from
Fat 23%

14	ounce can artichoke hearts, drained
2	cloves crushed garlic
1	small chopped onion
2	tablespoons olive oil
3	tablespoons fresh chopped parsley
1/2	teaspoon basil
1/2	teaspoon salt
1/2	teaspoon black pepper, fresh ground
1/4	cup grated Parmesan cheese
2	egg whites
1/2	pound spaghetti

Rinse and quarter the canned artichoke hearts. Heat the olive oil in a skillet and sauté the onion and garlic for 3-4 minutes. Add 1/2 cup water, parsley, basil, salt and pepper. Simmer for 15 minutes. Boil a large pot of salted water and cook the spaghetti for 8-10 minutes or until cooked. Combine the egg whites and parmesan cheese. Toss the pasta in the mixture. Add the artichoke mixture and reheat. Add extra water if it is too dry. Serve with extra Parmesan cheese as a topping.

Notes: Excellent source of Vitamin C, B12, B2, Folacin, Niacin and Iron. Good source of Vitamin B6, Calcium and Zinc.

Stir-fry Vegetables and Rice

1	medium chopped onion
1	peeled and chopped carrot
1	cup mung bean sprouts
1	cup bok choy, sliced thick
1/4	cup slivered almonds
2	tablespoons soy sauce
1/2	teaspoon black pepper, fresh ground
1/2	red bell pepper
2	sliced water chestnuts
1	teaspoon sesame oil
2	cups cooked brown rice

Serving Size: 4
Prep Time: 0:10

Total Calories 210
Protein 6g
Carbohydrate 33g
Fat 7g
Cholesterol 0mg
Dietary Fiber 3g
% Calories from
Fat 28%

Heat the sesame oil in a large wok or deep skillet. Add the chopped onion and carrot and stir-fry for 2 minutes. Add the other vegetables and continue to stir-fry for 3-4 minutes more. Add the almonds, soy sauce and pepper. Serve with the cooked rice.

Notes: Excellent source of Vitamin C, A, B6 and Folacin.
Good source of Vitamin B1, Niacin and Zinc.

Tasty Rice and Tofu

Serving Size: 6
Prep Time: 0:20

Total Calories 198
Protein 9g
Carbohydrate 32g
Fat 4g
Cholesterol 0mg
Dietary Fiber 3g
% Calories from
Fat 17%

1 1/2	pounds tofu, low-fat
1/2	tablespoon olive oil
2	cloves crushed garlic
2	medium chopped onions
1	cup sliced mushrooms
1/3	cup Tamari soy sauce
dash	Tabasco sauce
1	teaspoon fresh chopped basil
1/2	teaspoon thyme
1/4	teaspoon marjoram
1/4	teaspoon savory
2	cups vegetable broth
2	cups cooked rice

Heat the olive oil in a nonstick skillet. Add the garlic and onions and sauté for 3-5 minutes until transparent. Add the mushrooms and cook 2 more minutes, shaking the skillet constantly. Remove the vegetables and set aside on a warm dish. Cut the tofu into 1 1/2" size cubes. In a mixing bowl combine the Tamari, basil, thyme, savory, marjoram and Tabasco. Dip the tofu cubes in the mixture and brown the cubes in the skillet. Add the vegetable broth to the skillet and return the vegetable mixture. Simmer for 10 minutes and serve hot with rice as a main dish.

Notes: Excellent source of Vitamin A and Iron. Good source of Vitamin B6, B1, B2, Folacin, Niacin, Calcium and Zinc.

Chicken Cacciatore

Serving Size: 4
Prep Time: 1:00

Total Calories 221
Protein 24g
Carbohydrate 19
Fat 4g
Cholesterol 51mg
Dietary Fiber 4g
% Calories from
Fat 17%

4	boneless skinless chicken breast halves
1/2	tablespoon olive oil
2	medium onions, sliced 1/4" thick
2	cloves crushed garlic
14	ounces canned tomatoes
8	ounces tomato paste
1/2	teaspoon salt
1/4	teaspoon black pepper, fresh ground
1	teaspoon fresh chopped oregano
1	teaspoon fresh thyme
1/4	teaspoon celery seed
1	bay leaf
1/2	cup white wine

Heat the oil in a large non-stick heavy skillet. Sauté the onion and garlic for 3-4 minutes, remove and set aside. Dust the chicken breasts in flour and brown for 5-6 minutes. Return the onion and garlic to the skillet. Mix the rest of the ingredients except the wine together in a mixing bowl and add to the skillet. Cover and simmer for 30 minutes. Add the wine and cook uncovered for 15 minutes. Remove the bay leaf and any excess fat. Serve with mashed potato or pasta as a main dish.

Notes: Excellent source of Vitamin C, A, B6, Niacin and Iron. Good source of Vitamin B1, B2, Folacin, Calcium and Zinc.

Poultry

Chicken Curry

6	boneless skinless chicken breast halves
1 1/2	cups chicken broth
5	teaspoons Worcestershire sauce
5	crushed bay leaves
1/2	teaspoon Tabasco sauce
6	teaspoons curry powder
3	teaspoons oregano
1	teaspoon paprika
2	cloves crushed garlic

Serving Size: 6
Prep Time: 0:10
Baking Time: 0:50

Total Calories 139
Protein 24g
Carbohydrate 4g
Fat 3g
Cholesterol 52mg
Dietary Fiber 1g
% Calories from
Fat 17%

Preheat the oven to 350°F. Combine all the ingredients except the chicken breasts in a pan and bring to the boil. Place the chicken in a ovenproof dish and cover with the mixture. Cover the dish and bake for 50 minutes or until done.

Notes: Excellent source of Vitamin B6 and Niacin.

Chicken in Soy Sauce

4	skinless chicken legs
I	cup soy sauce
2	tablespoons honey
I	clove crushed garlic
3-4	green onions sliced diagonally

Serving Size: 4
Prep Time: 1:00
Marinate Time: 2:00+

Total Calories 234
Protein 32g
Carbohydrate 14g
Fat 5g
Cholesterol 113mg
Dietary Fiber <1g
% Calories from
Fat 21%

Combine the soy sauce, honey and garlic. Marinate the chicken legs for at least 2 hours or overnight. Bake in a covered dish for one hour at 350°F. Serve with rice or mashed potatoes. Sprinkle with onions.

Notes: Excellent source of Vitamin B6, B2 and Niacin. Good source of Vitamin B1 and Folacin.

Chicken with Tarragon

2	pounds chicken, skinless light meat
1/2	tablespoon butter
1/2	tablespoon olive oil
4	sprigs fresh tarragon
1/2	teaspoon salt
1/2	teaspoon black pepper, fresh ground
1	clove crushed garlic

Serving Size: 4
Prep Time: 0:30

Total Calories 166
Protein 27g
Carbohydrate 2g
Fat 5g
Cholesterol 70mg
Dietary Fiber <1g
% Calories from
Fat 28%

Preheat the oven to 325°F. Crush the garlic into the butter and oil and mix together. Smear this mixture over the breasts of the chicken. Place one sprig of tarragon inside each of the pieces and place them in a baking dish. Cover with a piece of aluminum foil leaving the sides open. Place in the oven for 20 minutes, turning twice. Remove the foil and brown for 5 more minutes or until cooked. Serve with a green salad.

Notes: Excellent source of Vitamin B6 and Niacin. Good source of Vitamin B2 and Iron.

Cider-Basted Chicken

Serving Size: 6
Prep Time: 0:25
Marinate Time 2:00+

Total Calories 211
Protein 23g
Carbohydrate 22g
Fat 4g
Cholesterol 51mg
Dietary Fiber 3g
% Calories from
Fat 17%

6	skinless boneless chicken breast halves
1	cup apple juice
1/2	cup lemon juice
1/4	cup brown sugar
2	fluid ounces low-sodium soy sauce
1	clove garlic
2	tablespoons olive oil
2	tablespoons fresh parsley
1	bay leaf
1/2	teaspoon salt
1/4	teaspoon black pepper
1	chopped carrot
2	cups zucchini
2	cups yellow squash

Combine liquid ingredients into a marinade. Add chicken breasts and marinate overnight (or for at least 30 minutes). Remove chicken from marinade and pat dry with a paper towel. Sauté the julienned carrots, zucchini and yellow squash, add the chicken breasts and bake in the oven at 350°F for 20 minutes until the chicken and vegetables are cooked and tender. Serve with rice as a main dish.

Notes: Excellent source of Vitamin C, A, B6, Folacin and Niacin. Good source of Vitamin B1, B2, Iron and Zinc.

Coq au Vin

1	pound cut chicken, skinless dark meat,
2	pounds cut chicken, skinless light meat,
1/2	tablespoon butter
1/2	slice bacon
1/2	tablespoon olive oil
12	white pearl onions
12	button mushrooms
1	cup red wine
2	bay leaves
2	cloves crushed garlic
2	tablespoons fresh chopped parsley
1	teaspoon thyme
1/2	teaspoon salt
1/4	teaspoon black pepper, fresh ground

Serving Size: 6
Prep Time: 0:10
Baking Time: 0:45

Total Calories 320
Protein 51g
Carbohydrate 1g
Fat 8g
Cholesterol 151mg
Dietary Fiber 1g
% Calories from
Fat 25%

Preheat the oven to 375°F. Cut the chicken into serving size pieces. Heat the oil in a large non-stick casserole dish. Add the bacon and when brown add the onions and cook for 1-2 minutes. Stir in the mushrooms and remove from the casserole dish and keep warm. Roll the chicken pieces in seasoned flour and brown in the casserole dish. Return the vegetables to the dish and add the bay leaves, thyme, salt and pepper. Cover the dish and place in the oven for 45 minutes or until the chicken is tender. Remove the bay leaves. Remove the chicken and vegetables and place on a covered dish in a warming oven. Skim excess fat from the sauce and add the red wine. Boil the sauce so it reduces by about half. Thicken it with one tablespoon corn flour dissolved in water or a beurre manie (1/2 tablespoon butter mixed with 1/2 tablespoon flour). Strain the sauce into a clean casserole dish and add back the chicken and vegetables. Cover and leave in a very slow oven until ready to serve. Garnish with finely chopped parsley.

Notes: Excellent source of Vitamin B6, B12, B1, B2 and Niacin. Good source of Iron.

Lemon Chicken with English Walnuts

Serving Size: 4
Prep Time: 0:10
Baking Time: 0:20

Total Calories 166
Protein 27g
Carbohydrate 5g
Fat 4g
Cholesterol 65mg
Dietary Fiber <1g
% Calories from
Fat 21%

4	skinless chicken breast halves
2	tablespoons fresh lemon juice
2	tablespoons chopped English walnuts
2	tablespoons soy sauce
1	tablespoon corn flour
1/4	teaspoon white pepper

Preheat the oven to 325°F. Dissolve the corn flour in the soy sauce and lemon juice. Add the white pepper and chopped walnuts. Heat a non-stick skillet sprayed with olive oil and add the chicken breast halves. Brown for 2-3 minutes on each side. Remove and set aside on a warm serving dish. Add the sauce and allow the corn flour to thicken. Adjust the consistency if desired. Pour over the chicken and place in oven for 20 minutes. Serve hot.

Notes: Excellent source of Vitamin B6 and Niacin. Good source of Vitamin B1 and Zinc.

Oven-baked Sesame Chicken

4	skinless chicken breast halves
1/2	cup flour
1/4	cup sesame seeds
1/4	teaspoon garlic powder
1/4	teaspoon black pepper, fresh ground
1/2	teaspoon paprika
1/2	teaspoon salt
1/4	cup 1% low-fat milk

Serving Size: 4
Prep Time: 0:10
Baking Time: 0:45

Total Calories 243
Protein 31g
Carbohydrate 14g
Fat 7g
Cholesterol 66mg
Dietary Fiber <1g
% Calories from
Fat 25%

Toast sesame seeds in a skillet until golden brown, stirring constantly. Preheat the oven to 400°F. Lightly oil a shallow baking pan. Combine flour, sesame seeds, garlic powder, black pepper, paprika and salt in a bag and shake well. Dip the chicken in milk and then coat in the bag. Place chicken in baking pan and bake for 45 minutes until golden brown.

Notes: Excellent source of Vitamin B6, B1 and Niacin. Good source of Vitamin B2, Folacin and Zinc.

Turkey Breast in White Wine

Serving Size: 4
Prep Time: 0:20

Total Calories 146
Protein 12g
Carbohydrate 14g
Fat 4g
Cholesterol 17mg
Dietary Fiber <1g
% Calories from
Fat 25%

8	turkey breast slices
12	chopped shallots
1	cup dry white wine
1/4	cup sliced mushrooms
1	clove crushed garlic
1/4	teaspoon salt
1/4	teaspoon black pepper, fresh ground

Spray a skillet with olive oil and sauté the shallots. Add the mushrooms and garlic and continue to simmer in the covered skillet. Add the wine and bring to the boil. Simmer and allow the mixture to reduce by about half. Add the sliced turkey breast and cover. Simmer for a further 5 minutes or until the turkey is cooked. Serve hot with mashed potatoes.

Notes: Excellent source of Vitamin A, B6, B12 and Niacin.
Good source of Vitamin C and Folacin.

Turkey Loaf

1 1/2	pounds ground turkey, white meat
1/4	cup chicken or turkey broth
1/2	tablespoon olive oil
3/4	cup bread crumbs
1	medium chopped onion
1/2	pound sliced mushrooms
2	cloves crushed garlic
1	tablespoon soy sauce
1	teaspoon thyme
2	tablespoons fresh chopped parsley
1/2	teaspoon marjoram
1/4	cup liquid egg substitute
1/2	teaspoon salt
1/2	teaspoon black pepper, fresh ground

Serving Size: 4
Prep Time: 0:10
Baking Time: 1:00

Total Calories 148
Protein 8g
Carbohydrate 21g
Fat 4g
Cholesterol 30mg
Dietary Fiber 3g
% Calories from
Fat 24%

Preheat the oven to 350°F. Heat the olive oil in a non-stick skillet. Sauté the onion and garlic for 2-3 minutes. Add the mushrooms and cook for another 2-3 minutes. In a large bowl combine the ground turkey, broth, bread crumbs, egg and sautéed vegetables. Place the mixture in a loaf pan and bake for 60 minutes. Serve sliced, hot or cold.

Notes: Good source of Vitamin A, B6, B1, B2, Niacin and Iron.

Turkey Burgers Southwestern Style

1	pound ground skinless turkey light meat
1	pound sliced mushrooms
2	cups salsa
4	hamburger buns

Serving Size: 4
Prep Time: 0:15

Total Calories 335
Protein 30g
Carbohydrate 30g
Fat 9g
Cholesterol 69mg
Dietary Fiber 2g
% Calories from
Fat 25%

Combine the ground turkey and 1/4 cup of salsa in a mixing bowl. Form into 4 patties. Brush with a little oil and broil for 4-5 minutes on each side. Sauté the mushrooms in a skillet sprayed with a little oil for 2-3 minutes until brown. Remove and spread on the turkey patties. Serve with extra salsa on hamburger rolls and a side salad.

Notes: Excellent source of Vitamin B6, B12, B1, B2, Folacin, Niacin, Iron and Zinc. Good source of Vitamin C and A.

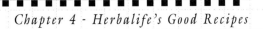

Salad and Relishes

3 Bean Mexican Salad

1	can green beans
1	can garbanzo beans
1	can kidney beans
1	cup chopped green pepper
1/2	cup chopped red onion
1	cup cider vinegar
1	cup sugar
1 1/2	teaspoons salt
1/2	teaspoon pepper
1/3	cup olive oil
1	package taco seasoning mix

Serving Size: 8
Prep Time: 0:00

Total Calories 364
Protein 10.8g
Carbohydrate 59.4g
Fat 10.8g
Cholesterol 0mg
Dietary Fiber 11g
% Calories form Fat 25%

Drain canned beans and combine with green pepper and onion. Set aside. Combine remaining ingredients except taco seasoning. Pour over vegetables, mixing well. Cover and marinate in refrigerator overnight or 24 hours, stirring occasionally. Before serving, drain, leaving small amount of marinade to toss taco seasoning with salad.

Notes: Excellent source of Vitamin C, B1, Folacin and Iron. Good source of Vitamin B6 and Zinc.

Carrot and Raisin Salad

3	shredded medium carrots
1/2	cup seedless raisins
1/2	cup orange juice
1	tablespoon lemon juice
1	teaspoon olive oil

Serving Size: 4
Prep Time: 0:10

Mix together the fruit juice and oil. Add the carrots and raisins. Serve chilled as a side salad.

Notes: Excellent source of Vitamin C and A. Good source of Folacin.

Total Calories 102
Protein 2g
Carbohydrate 23g
Fat 1g
Cholesterol 0g
Dietary Fiber 2g
% Calories from
Fat 11%

Chef's Salad

1	head dark green lettuce
1/4	pound cooked white chicken meat
1/4	pound low fat ham
1/4	pound low fat Swiss cheese
2	hard-boiled eggs
4	red ripe medium tomatoes
1	cup watercress
1	tablespoon olive oil
2	teaspoons Balsamic vinegar

Serving Size: 6
Prep Time: 0:20

Total Calories 174
Protein 17g
Carbohydrate 8g
Fat 8g
Cholesterol 99mg
Dietary Fiber 3g
% Calories from
Fat 43%

Chop the washed lettuce and place in the bottom of a salad bowl. Add the chicken, ham and cheese. Garnish with wedges of egg, tomatoes and sprigs of watercress. Serve chilled, dressed with the oil and vinegar and seasoned to taste.

Notes: Excellent source of Vitamin C, A, B6, B12, B1, B2, Folacin, Niacin and Calcium. Good source of Iron and Zinc.

Citrus Salad

6	oranges
2	grapefruit
2	heads radicchio
2	tablespoons fresh orange juice
2	teaspoons Balsamic vinegar
pinch	salt
pinch	white pepper
1	tablespoon extra virgin olive oil

Peel and section the oranges and grapefruit by cutting into the center to make wedges and removing the thick section walls. Arrange the sections alternately on top of a bed of radicchio leaves. Combine the orange juice, Balsamic vinegar, salt, pepper and olive oil and pour over the salad just prior to serving.

Notes: Excellent source of Vitamin C. Good source of Vitamin B1 and Calcium.

This salad looks even more attractive if made with blood oranges and ruby citrus grapefruit.

Serving Size: 6
Prep Time: 0:10

Total Calories 100
Protein 2g
Carbohydrate 27g
Fat 3g
Cholesterol 0mg
Dietary Fiber 4g
% Calories from Fat 17%

Cole Slaw

1	medium (1pound) cabbage head
1	shredded medium carrot
2	tablespoons water
1/8	cup sugar
1/2	cup vinegar
1/2	medium green bell pepper, chopped
1/4	cup green onions, sliced thin
1/2	teaspoon celery seed
1/2	teaspoon mustard seed

Serving Size: 6
Prep Time: 0:15
Marinate Time: 24:00

Total Calories 65
Protein 2g
Carbohydrate 16g
Fat <1g
Cholesterol 0mg
Dietary Fiber 6g
% Calories from
Fat 5%

Finely shred the cabbage. Add the carrot, celery, green pepper, onions and seeds. Mix well. Heat the sugar, water and vinegar in a pan until boiling. Boil for 2 minutes, then let cool to room temperature. Add vinegar mixture to the vegetables and mix well. Cover and refrigerate for 24 hours. Serve drained from the liquid.

Notes: Excellent source of Vitamin C, A and Folacin. Good source of Vitamin B6.

German Potato Salad

2	pounds new potatoes
1	tablespoon sugar
2	tablespoons white wine vinegar
1/4	pint light sour cream
1	teaspoon mustard
1/2	medium chopped onion
1	teaspoon celery seed
1	teaspoon lemon juice
pinch	salt
pinch	black pepper

Serving Size: 4
Prep Time: 0:30

Total Calories 74
Protein 2g
Carbohydrate 15g
Fat <1g
Cholesterol 2mg
Dietary Fiber 1g
% Calories from
Fat 9%

Scrape the potatoes and place in a pan of cold water. Bring to boil and cook until tender (5-10 minutes). Drain and slice into even-sized pieces. Combine the cream, mustard, sugar, vinegar and celery seed. Peel and chop the onion and add to the mixture. Bind the potatoes with the sauce and chill for at least 2 hours. Serve garnished with chopped chives or parsley.

Notes: Excellent source of Vitamin C. Good source of
Vitamin B6.

Greek Salad

Serving Size: 4
Prep Time: 0:10

Total Calories 110
Protein 5g
Carbohydrate 12g
Fat 6g
Cholesterol 13mg
Dietary Fiber 4g
% Calories from
Fat 45%

1	medium lettuce
2	ounces feta cheese
3	Greek olives
2	red ripe medium tomatoes, chopped
1	small sliced cucumber
3	medium chopped radishes
1	chopped green bell pepper
1/2	tablespoon olive oil
1	teaspoon red wine vinegar
pinch	salt
pinch	black pepper

Combine the oil, vinegar, salt and pepper in the base of a wooden salad bowl. Add the lettuce, tomatoes, cucumber, radishes, bell pepper and olives. Toss and place on a serving dish. Crumble feta cheese on the top.

Notes: Excellent source of Vitamin C, A and Folacin. Good source of Vitamin B6, B1, B2, Calcium and Iron.

Green Tomato Relish

12	green tomatoes
9	medium onions
1/3	cup salt
4	green bell peppers, seeded and chopped
4	red bell peppers, seeded and chopped
4	gherkins
1	tablespoon celery seed
4	cups sugar
1	quart vinegar

Serving Size: 16
Prep Time: 0:30

Total Calories 255
Protein 2g
Carbohydrate 65g
Fat <1g
Cholesterol 0mg
Dietary Fiber 3g
% Calories from
Fat 1%

Chop the onions and the tomatoes and mix together. This may be done in a blender or food processor. Add the salt, cover with the water and set aside for 10 minutes to draw the fluids out of the vegetables. Drain and place in a large saucepan. Add the bell peppers, chili peppers, gherkins (canned or bottled pickles may be used), celery seed, sugar and vinegar. Bring to boil and simmer for 15 minutes. Place in pickle jars and seal while still hot.

Notes: Excellent source of Vitamin A, C and B6. Good source of Folacin.

Provençale Salad

Serving Size: 6
Prep Time: 0:45

Total Calories 98
Protein 3g
Carbohydrate 12g
Fat 5g
Cholesterol 1mg
Dietary Fiber 3g
% Calories from
Fat 46%

2	green bell peppers, sliced thin
2	red bell peppers, sliced thin
6	red ripe tomatoes, chopped
1	yellow bell pepper, sliced thin
2	anchovies
4	sliced black olives
1	tablespoon chopped parsley
1	tablespoon chopped tarragon
1	tablespoon chopped chervil
1	tablespoon chopped chives
1	tablespoon olive oil
1	tablespoon red wine vinegar
1/4	teaspoon salt
1/4	teaspoon black pepper, finely ground

Roast the peppers over a flame or on a grill. Remove the skins, seeds and core and slice into thick strips. Slice the tomatoes and place on a large, flat serving dish. Add the peppers and arrange in layers according to color. Combine the oil and vinegar with the herbs and season to taste. Sprinkle the dressing over the vegetables and chill for at least 30 minutes before serving.

Notes: Excellent source of Vitamin C, A and Folacin. Good
source of Vitamin B6 and Iron.

Russian Salad

1	pound new potatoes
1/2	pound sliced string beans
4	medium sliced carrots
1	cup cooked white beans
1	cup green peas
2	tablespoons red wine vinegar
1	tablespoon olive oil
1	tablespoon capers
1	tablespoon finely chopped parsley
2	hard-boiled eggs, whites only
1/2	cup low-fat mayonnaise

Serving Size: 6
Prep Time: 0:20
Standing Time: 1:00+

Total Calories 272
Protein 13g
Carbohydrate 46g
Fat 5g
Cholesterol 10mg
Dietary Fiber 10g
% Calories from
Fat 16%

Cook the potatoes and cool. Steam the string beans and slice evenly. Place the beans, carrots, white beans and green peas in a large mixing bowl and add the potatoes. Mix the vinegar and olive oil in a small bowl and season to taste with salt and pepper. Add the dressing to the vegetables and combine lightly. Separate the hard-boiled eggs and chop the whites. Add the egg whites, capers and mayonnaise to the vegetable mixture and arrange in a salad bowl. Sieve the egg yolks and sprinkle on the top as a garnish. Serve with extra parsley and lemon wedges.

Notes: Excellent source of Vitamin C, A, B6, B1, Folacin and Iron. Good source of Vitamin B2, Calcium and Zinc.

Summer Vegetable and Rice Salad

Serving Size: 6
Prep Time: 0:20

Total Calories 364
Protein 7g
Carbohydrate 75g
Fat 3g
Cholesterol 0mg
Dietary Fiber 12g
% Calories from
Fat 7%

3	cups cooked rice
1	tablespoon olive oil
1	teaspoon Balsamic vinegar
1	medium chopped bell pepper
1	tablespoon chopped celery
1	tablespoon chopped parsley
2	chopped scallions
2	tablespoon chopped chives
3	tablespoon chopped red bell pepper

Combine the ingredients in a large bowl and chill for at least one hour.

Notes: Excellent source of source of Vitamin A, C, B1, Niacin and Iron. Good source of Vitamin B6.

Tabbouleh

1 1/2	cups bulgur
4	cups boiling water, poured over bulgur
1/4	cup soaked garbanzo beans
1 1/2	cups chopped parsley
3/4	cup chopped mint
3/4	cup chopped scallions
1/2	cup lemon juice
1	tablespoon olive oil
1	teaspoon black pepper, fresh ground

Serving Size: 6
Prep Time: 0:10
Standing Time: 2:00+

Total Calories 254
Protein 11g
Carbohydrate 44g
Fat 6g
Cholesterol 0mg
Dietary Fiber 10g
% Calories from
Fat 21%

Soak beans, cook until soft and drain. Pour boiling water over the bulgur wheat and let stand for 2 hours until light and puffy. Remove excess water by placing through a strainer. Combine with the herbs, lemon juice and olive oil. Chill for 1 hour.

Notes: Excellent source of Vitamin C, A, Folacin, Niacin, Calcium and Iron. Good source of Vitamin B6, B1 and Zinc.

Sandwiches

Cheese and Chutney Sandwich

2   ounces cheddar cheese
1   tablespoon chutney
2   slices bread
1   small tomato, cut in quarters

Spread one slice of bread with melted butter substitute. Arrange the slices of cheese on top and cover with chutney. Close the sandwich with the other slice of bread and slice in half. Serve garnished with a slice of tomato and sprig of parsley for a hearty lunch

Notes: Excellent source of Vitamin A, C, B2, Folacin and Calcium. Good source of Zinc.

Serving Size: 1
Prep Time: 0:05

Total Calories 208
Protein 15g
Carbohydrate 15g
Fat 4g
Cholesterol 60mg
Dietary Fiber <1g
% Calories from Fat 25%

Grilled Chicken Breast Sandwich

Serving Size: 1
Prep Time: 0:05

Total Calories 243
Protein 21g
Carbohydrate 32g
Fat 3g
Cholesterol 40mg
Dietary Fiber 3g
% Calories from
Fat 12%

3	ounces grilled skinless chicken breast
2	bread slices
1	teaspoon low-fat mayonnaise
1	slice tomato

Spread mayonnaise on the bread and lay chicken breast and tomato on top. Serve garnished with tomato and pickle.

Notes: Good source of Vitamin C, B6, B1, B2, Folacin and Niacin. Good source of Vitamin A and Iron.

Chicken Salad Sandwich

Serving Size: 1
Prep Time: 0:05

Total Calories 314
Protein 32g
Carbohydrate 35g
Fat 5g
Cholesterol 66mg
Dietary Fiber 8g
% Calories from
Fat 3%

1/2	cup skinless light chicken meat, cubed
1	tablespoon low-fat mayonnaise
1/2	teaspoon chopped celery
1	small tomato
2	slices whole grain bread

Combine the chicken with mayonnaise and celery and place between two slices of bread. Cut in half and serve on a plate, garnished with quartered tomato and a sprig of parsley.

Notes: Excellent source of Vitamin C, B1, B2, Folacin, Niacin and Iron. Good source of A and Zinc.

English Cucumber Sandwich

4	slices white bread
1/2	cucumber
1	tablespoon butter substitute
	salt and pepper

Serving Size: 1
Prep Time: 0:05

Total Calories 38
Protein 1g
Carbohydrate 4g
Fat <1g
Cholesterol 1mg
Dietary Fiber <1g
% Calories from
Fat 13%

Spread thinly sliced white bread with butter or butter substitute. Peel and very thinly slice the cucumber. Arrange the cucumber slices on the buttered bread and season with salt and pepper. Place another slice of bread on top. Slice the crusts off into four even quarters. Arrange on a plate garnished with curled cucumber peel and serve with tea. This is a traditional English summer tea dish.

Notes: Good source of Vitamin C and Folacin.

Grilled Vegetable Italian Style Sandwich

1	slice Italian bread
1/2	medium eggplant
1/2	small yellow bell pepper
1/2	small red bell pepper
1	teaspoon extra virgin olive oil

Brush the grill or a ridged pan with olive oil and brown the vegetables quickly. Brown the Italian bread on one side and dribble the olive oil on the uncooked side. Arrange the grilled vegetables on top of the bread and serve warm.

Notes: Excellent source of Vitamin A, C, B6, B1, Folacin and Niacin. Good source of Vitamin B2 and Iron.

Serving Size: 1
Prep Time: 0:10

Total Calories 216
Protein 6g
Carbohydrate 37g
Fat 6g
Cholesterol 0mg
Dietary Fiber 7g
% Calories from Fat 24%

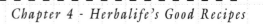

Chapter 4 - Herbalife's Good Recipes

Tuna Sandwich on Rye

1/2	cup tuna in water, drained
1	tablespoon low-fat mayonnaise
1	teaspoon mustard
1/2	teaspoon black pepper, fresh ground
2	slices rye bread

Serving Size: 1

Spread the slices of rye bread with mustard. Combine the tuna with mayonnaise and season with fresh ground black pepper. Spread the tuna mixture between the slices of rye bread and serve garnished with a dill pickle.

Notes: Excellent source of Vitamin B1, B2, Niacin, Folacin and Iron. Good source of Zinc.

Total Calories 302
Protein 29g
Carbohydrate 27g
Fat 4g
Cholesterol 27mg
Dietary Fiber 4g
% Calories from
Fat 12%

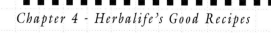

Sauces and Salad Dressings

Cucumber and Yogurt Dressing

1	cup plain, nonfat yogurt
1	medium cucumber, peeled and chopped
1	teaspoon sugar
1/2	tablespoon olive oil
1/4	teaspoon garlic powder
1/4	teaspoon black pepper, fresh ground
1	tablespoon white wine vinegar

Serving Size: 4
Prep Time: 0:10

Total Calories 62
Protein 4g
Carbohydrate 7g
Fat 3g
Cholesterol 1g
Dietary Fiber <1g
% Calories from
Fat 25%

Add cucumber to yogurt and combine with sugar, olive oil, garlic powder and seasonings. Stir in vinegar and chill before serving.

Notes: Good source of Calcium. Cucumber may be blended if preferred.

Curry Yogurt Dressing

1	cup plain, nonfat yogurt
1	tablespoon finely chopped scallions
1	tablespoon lemon juice
1	teaspoon cumin powder
2	teaspoons curry powder
pinch	salt
pinch	black pepper, fresh ground

Combine ingredients and chill before serving.

Notes: Good source of Calcium.

Serving Size: 4
Prep Time: 0:10

Total Calories 36
Protein 3g
Carbohydrate 5g
Fat <1g
Cholesterol 1g
Dietary Fiber <1g
% Calories from
Fat 6%

Lemon Tahini Dressing

1/2	cup olive oil
4	tablespoons lemon juice
1	clove crushed garlic
1	medium chopped onion
2	stalks chopped celery
2	tablespoons chopped parsley
pinch	salt
1/2	cup tahini

Serving Size: 8
Prep Time: 0:10

Total Calories 225
Protein 3g
Carbohydrate 6g
Fat 22g
Cholesterol 0g
Dietary Fiber 1g
% Calories from
Fat 83%

Combine the ingredients in a blender, adding the tahini last.
Serve chilled.

Notes: Excellent source of Iron. Good source of Vitamin C,
B6, Folacin and Zinc.

Marinara Sauce

1	teaspoon extra virgin olive oil
2	small chopped onions
2	16 ounce canned tomatoes
2	cloves crushed garlic
1/2	teaspoon finely chopped fresh thyme
	salt and pepper

Heat the olive oil in a large skillet. Sauté the onions and garlic for 3-4 minutes until transparent. Add the tomatoes and stir until mashed. Season with thyme, salt and pepper. Simmer over low heat for 20 minutes. Adjust with extra hot water if needed to reach desired pouring consistency. Serve hot over fresh cooked pasta.

Notes: Excellent source of Vitamin C. Good source of Vitamin A, B6.

Optional Additions: 2 ounces peeled shrimp, 2 ounces clams or other seafood.

Serving Size: 4
Prep Time: 0:30

Total Calories 51
Protein 2g
Carbohydrate 9g
Fat 1g
Cholesterol 0g
Dietary Fiber 2g
% Calories from
Fat 24%

Mustard and Dill Sauce

1/2	cup Dijon mustard
1	tablespoon honey
1	tablespoon fresh chopped dill
2	tablespoons water
1	tablespoon extra virgin olive oil
1	tablespoon white wine

Combine the ingredients in a mixing bowl. Serve with salmon, gravlax and other fish.

Serving Size: 4
Prep Time: 0:10

Total Calories 72
Protein 2g
Carbohydrate 7g
Fat 5g
Cholesterol 0g
Dietary Fiber <1g
% Calories from
Fat 50%

Oriental Dressing

2	tablespoons sesame oil
2	tablespoons rice vinegar
2	tablespoons soy sauce
1	clove crushed garlic
1/4	teaspoon ginger

Combine the ingredients in a mixing bowl.

Serving Size: 4
Prep Time: 0:10

Total Calories 66
Protein <1g
Carbohydrate <1g
Fat 6g
Cholesterol 0g
Dietary Fiber <1g
% Calories from
Fat 82%

Salsa

3	plum tomatoes, peeled and chopped
1	chopped onion
2	tablespoons fresh chopped cilantro
2	cloves crushed garlic
1	tablespoon fresh lime juice
1/2	teaspoon black pepper, fresh ground
1/2	teaspoon salt
1	small green chili pepper

Serving Size: 4
Prep Time: 0:15

Total Calories 11
Protein <1g
Carbohydrate 3g
Fat <1g
Cholesterol 0g
Dietary Fiber <1g
% Calories from
Fat 6%

Combine all ingredients except the salt in a bowl. Add the salt at the last minute. Serve freshly made with blue corn chips.

Notes: Excellent source of Vitamin C.

Sour Cream and Bacon Dressing

1	cup nonfat sour cream
1	tablespoon rice wine vinegar
1	tablespoon fat-free bacon bits
1	teaspoon prepared horseradish
pinch	salt
pinch	black pepper ground

Combine ingredients and chill before serving.

Serving Size: 4
Prep Time: 0:10

Total Calories 30
Protein 2g
Carbohydrate 2g
Fat <1g
Cholesterol 5mg
Dietary Fiber 0g
% Calories from
Fat <1%

Spicy Yogurt Dressing

1	cup yogurt, skim milk
1	tablespoon tomato paste
1/8	teaspoon celery salt
1	teaspoon Worcestershire sauce
	dash tabasco sauce
1	clove crushed garlic
1	teaspoon honey

Mix ingredients with a metal spoon or in the blender.

Notes: Good source of Calcium.

Serving Size: 4
Prep Time: 0:10

Total Calories 42
Protein 4g
Carbohydrate 7g
Fat <1g
Cholesterol 1mg
Dietary Fiber <1g
% Calories from
Fat 3%

Tarragon Sauce for Fish

4	tablespoons tarragon, finely chopped
2	tablespoons olive oil
1/4	cup butter
1	cup lemon juice

Mix ingredients in a small pan, melting the butter. Serve hot over barbecued or broiled fish.

Notes: Excellent source of Vitamin A and C. Good source of Calcium and Iron.

Serving Size: 2
Prep Time: 0:10

Total Calories 178
Protein 3g
Carbohydrate 15g
Fat 14g
Cholesterol 0mg
Dietary Fiber 1g
% Calories from
Fat 64%

Vinaigrette

2	tablespoons olive oil
1	tablespoon Balsamic vinegar
1	clove crushed garlic
1	teaspoon Dijon mustard
1	teaspoon honey
pinch	salt
1/8	teaspoon black pepper, fresh ground

Serving Size: 4
Prep Time: 0:10

Total Calories 68
Protein <1g
Carbohydrate 2g
Fat 7g
Cholesterol 0g
Dietary Fiber <1g
% Calories from
Fat 87%

Mix ingredients with a fork. Traditional French vinaigrette is mixed in the bottom of the salad bowl before adding the lettuce.

Warm Coriander Sauce

Serving Size: 6
Prep Time: 0:10
Stand Time: 1:00

Total Calories 38
Protein 1g
Carbohydrate 4g
Fat 2g
Cholesterol 0g
Dietary Fiber <1g
% Calories from
Fat 52%

1	tablespoon olive oil
1/4	cup tomato juice
1/2	teaspoon paprika
1/4	teaspoon cayenne
1	teaspoon ground cumin
2	cloves crushed garlic
1/4	cup lemon juice
1/4	cup chopped parsley
1/4	cup chopped coriander (cilantro) leaves

Combine all of the ingredients together and refrigerate for 1 hour. Warm slightly. Serve spooned over broiled fish.

Notes: Excellent source of Vitamin C. Good source of Vitamin A and Iron.

Soups and Broths

Chicken and Okra Gumbo

2	skinless boneless chicken breast halves
2	tablespoons olive oil
2	cups chopped okra1
1	medium chopped onion
2	sticks chopped celery
1	medium chopped green bell pepper
1	15 ounce chopped can tomatoes
4	cloves crushed garlic
1	tablespoon Worcestershire sauce
1/2	teaspoon Creole seasoning
1/2	cup cooked rice
3	quarts water

GARNISH

1/4	teaspoon filé (optional)
1	tablespoon chopped scallions

Heat half of the oil in a heavy-bottomed casserole dish. Dust the chicken with flour and brown for 4-6 minutes on each side. Remove and set aside in a warm place. Add the rest of the oil and sauté the okra for 10 minutes stirring constantly. Add the onion, celery, bell pepper and garlic and continue to cook for 1-2 minutes. Add the chicken, tomatoes, Worcestershire sauce, seasonings and water and bring to a boil. Reduce the heat, cover the pan and simmer for 2 hours or until the chicken is tender. Skim excess fat and serve with rice in soup bowls. Garnish with chopped scallions and a sprinkling of filé, if available.

Notes: Excellent source of Vitamin C, B6 and Folacin
Good source of Vitamin A, B1 and Niacin.

Serving Size: 6
Prep Time: 0:20
Cooking Time: 2:00

Total Calories 109
Protein 9g
Carbohydrate 13g
Fat 3g
Cholesterol 17mg
Dietary Fiber 2g
% Calories from
Fat 24%

Chicken Soup

3	pounds chicken, skinless light meat cut in pieces
4	quarts water
2	bay leaves
1/2	teaspoon pepper
1	teaspoon paprika
3	cloves crushed garlic
3	medium sliced carrots
3	stalks chopped celery
1	medium chopped onion
2	sliced leeks
2	sprigs parsley
1/2	tablespoon olive oil

Serving Size: 4
Prep Time:0:10
Cooking Time: 3:00

Total Calories 332
Protein 48g
Carbohydrate 25g
Fat 6g
Cholesterol 99mg
Dietary Fiber 6g
% Calories from Fat 16%

Heat the oil in a large, heavy based pan. Sauté the onions and garlic for 3-4 minutes. Add the water, paprika, salt, pepper and bay leaves. Bring to a boil, cover and simmer for 2 hours. Remove from the heat, cut the chicken into small pieces and remove the bones. Return the chicken to the pan and add the carrots, celery, onions and parsley. Simmer for another hour. Serve hot.

Notes: Excellent source of Vitamin C, A, B6, B12, B2, Niacin, Calcium, Iron and Zinc. Good source of Vitamin B1 and Folacin.

Serving Size: 4
Prep Time: 0:15

Total Calories 219
Protein 16g
Carbohydrate 34g
Fat 5g
Cholesterol 21mg
Dietary Fiber <1g
% Calories from
Fat 20%

Corn and Tuna Bisque

1	tablespoon butter
1	tablespoon flour
1/2	cup 1% low-fat milk
1	chicken bouillon cube
1	10 ounce can corn, drained
1	10 ounce can tuna in water, drained
1/2	teaspoon salt
1/2	teaspoon pepper
1	teaspoon curry powder

Melt the butter in a saucepan. Over gentle heat, add the flour and stir into a roux so that it comes away from the side of the pan. Add the milk and crumbled chicken bouillon cube and simmer until the sauce thickens. Stir in the drained corn and shredded tuna. Add the curry powder and seasonings and serve immediately.

Notes: Excellent source of Vitamin B6, B12 and Niacin.
Good source of Vitamin B1, B2, Iron and Zinc.

Gazpacho

1	clove crushed garlic
6	cups canned chopped tomatoes
1	medium chopped onion
1/2	cup chopped green pepper
1/2	cup chopped cucumber, chopped
1/4	cup finely ground bread crumbs
2	cups tomato juice
1/2	teaspoon cumin
1/2	teaspoon black pepper, fresh ground
1/2	teaspoon salt
1	tablespoon extra virgin olive oil
1/4	cup fresh lemon juice

Serving Size: 6
Prep Time: 0:10
Stand Time: 0:30

Total Calories 112
Protein 4g
Carbohydrate 20g
Fat 3g
Cholesterol 0mg
Dietary Fiber 4g
% Calories from
Fat 23%

Blend the tomatoes, garlic, onion and green pepper in a blender. Add the cucumber and strain into a serving bowl containing the bread crumbs. Mix well and chill for 30 minutes in the refrigerator. Before serving, blend the olive oil, lemon juice, salt, pepper, cumin and tomato juice. Stir into the mixture and serve garnished with small dishes of diced tomatoes, cucumber and green pepper.

Notes: Excellent source of Vitamin A, C, B6 and Folacin. Good source of Calcium.

Green Pea Soup

mServing Size: 6
Prep Time: 0:30

Total Calories 192
Protein 13g
Carbohydrate 33
Fat 2g
Cholesterol 0g
Dietary Fiber 14g
% Calories from
Fat 8%

1/2	tablespoon olive oil
2	medium chopped onions
2	stalks chopped celery
1 1/2	cups split peas, soaked overnight
4	cups water
1	teaspoon oregano
1	teaspoon black pepper, fresh ground
1/2	teaspoon salt
1/2	teaspoon dry mustard

Heat the oil in a saucepan and sauté the onions and celery for 3-4 minutes. Add the celery and cook for another 2 minutes. Add the water and peas and bring to a boil. Cover and simmer for 20 minutes or until the peas become mushy. Place in the blender or in a food processor with a metal blade to blend. Add oregano and adjust seasoning. Serve hot with croutons.

Notes: Excellent source of Vitamin B1 and Folacin. Good source of Vitamin B6, Iron and Zinc.

Immuno-Soup

1	cup beans (red kidney, pinto, etc.), soaked overnight or canned
2	whole carrots, sliced thin
1	whole beet, sliced
1	whole potato, diced
1	head celery, chopped
1	bunch parsley, chopped
1/2	pounds sliced green beans
4	whole zucchini, sliced thin
1	bunch sliced scallions
1	pounds chopped spinach
1/2	head cauliflower, broken in pieces
1	whole rutabaga, chopped
1	whole turnip, chopped
2	cloves crushed garlic
1/2	whole bell pepper, chopped
1/2	teaspoon oregano
1/2	teaspoon marjoram
1/2	teaspoon rosemary
1/2	teaspoon sage
1	teaspoon thyme

Serving Size: 8
Prep Time: 0:45

Total Calories 179
Protein 12g
Carbohydrate 35g
Fat 1g
Cholesterol 0mg
Dietary Fiber 13g
% Calories from
Fat 5%

Soak beans overnight and discard water. Wash and prepare the vegetables. Place the root vegetables (carrots, potatoes, turnip, parsnip or rutabaga) into a large pot with the beans. Half fill the pot with water and bring to a boil. Cover and simmer for 10 minutes. Add all of the other ingredients and season to taste. Return to a boil and cook uncovered for 1-2 minutes more. Cover and simmer for another 30 minutes.

Cont.

Adjust seasoning and serve hot or cold.

This soup improves with age. Split into to 1-2 cup-sized servings and freeze for a quick and healthy meal. You can add grated cheese to the surface of a bowl and melt it under a hot grill. For variety include brown rice, barley, noodles or corn. Tamari, soy sauce or Bragg's liquid aminos also add flavor.

Notes: Excellent source of Vitamin C, A, B6, B1, B2, Folacin, Calcium and Iron. Good source of Niacin and Zinc.

Serving Ideas: Serve with hot crusty bread.

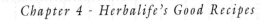

Minestrone

I	cup white beans, soaked
1/2	tablespoon olive oil
I	medium chopped onion
2	cloves crushed garlic
2	stalks chopped celery
3	medium diced carrots
I	medium diced green bell pepper
8	cups water
1/3	cup frozen green peas
1/2	cup frozen chopped green beans
1/2	teaspoon rosemary
1/2	teaspoon thyme
1/2	teaspoon oregano
1/2	teaspoon marjoram
1/2	cup cooked pasta shells
I	teaspoon salt
1/2	teaspoon black pepper, fresh ground

Serving Size: 6
Prep Time: 1:00

Total Calories 192
Protein 11g
Carbohydrate 35g
Fat 1g
Cholesterol 0mg
Dietary Fiber 8g
% Calories from
Fat 7%

Rinse the beans and boil for 20 minutes. Heat the oil in a non-stick skillet and sauté the onion and garlic for 3-4 minutes. Add the celery, carrots and green pepper and continue to cook for 1-2 minutes. Add the water, salt and pepper and bring to boil, cover and simmer for 15 minutes. Add the pasta shells, green beans and peas and continue to cook for 10 minutes. Serve hot.

Notes: Excellent source of Vitamin C, A, B1, Folacin and Iron.
Good source of Vitamin B6, Calcium and Zinc.

Phytomineral Soup

1	medium chopped onion
2	sticks chopped celery
4	cloves crushed garlic
1	teaspoon curry powder
2	medium sliced carrots
1/2	cup corn
1	15 ounce can tomatoes
1	packet vegetable bouillon cube
1	cup frozen peas
1/2	cup firm tofu
2	cups spinach leaves, chopped fine
1/2	cup chopped parsley
1	teaspoon thyme
1/2	teaspoon rosemary
1	tablespoon olive oil
5	cups water
pinch	salt
1/4	teaspoon black pepper, fresh ground

Serving Size: 6
Prep Time: 0:30

Total Calories 153
Protein 7g
Carbohydrate 23g
Fat 4g
Cholesterol 0mg
Dietary Fiber 4g
% Calories from
Fat 24%

Heat the oil in a large non-stick skillet. Sauté the onions and garlic for 3-5 minutes. Add the celery and carrots and sauté for a further 2 minutes. Add the corn, tomatoes, parsley, thyme, rosemary and sage. Dissolve the packet of vegetable broth in a cup of boiling water. Add to the pan with 4 more cups of water. Bring to a boil, cover and reduce the heat. Simmer for 20 minutes. Add the peas, tofu and spinach. Season to taste and simmer for 5 more minutes.

Notes: Excellent source of Vitamin C, A, B6, Folacin and Iron. Good source of Vitamin B1, B2, Niacin, Calcium and Zinc.

Rice and Celery Soup

6	sticks celery, finely chopped
I	cup rice
2	crumbled chicken bouillon cubes,
6	cups water
1/2	medium chopped onion
14	ounces canned chopped tomatoes
I	tablespoon extra virgin olive oil
1/2	teaspoon salt
1/3	cup fresh parsley, finely chopped
1/2	teaspoon black pepper, fresh ground

Serving Size: 6
Prep Time: 0:40

Total Calories 158
Protein 4g
Carbohydrate 30g
Fat 2g
Cholesterol 0mg
Dietary Fiber 2g
% Calories from
Fat 15%

Dissolve the chicken bouillon cubes in water and heat in a saucepan. In a skillet, heat the oil and sauté the onion and garlic for 3-4 minutes. Add the celery, tomatoes, salt and pepper. Cook on low heat, stirring frequently for 10-15 minutes. Add the rice and continue heating for 20 minutes or until the rice is cooked. Remove from heat, add the fresh parsley and serve.

Notes: Excellent source of Vitamin C. Good source of
Vitamin A, B6, B1, Folacin, Niacin and Iron.

Serving Size: 4
Prep Time: 0:40

Total Calories 82
Protein 2g
Carbohydrate 17g
Fat 1g
Cholesterol 0mg
Dietary Fiber 5g
% Calories from
Fat 14%

Root Vegetable Soup

2	carrots, peeled and diced
1	turnip, peeled and diced
1	rutabaga, peeled and diced
1	parsnip, peeled and diced
1	chopped onion
2	cloves crushed garlic
1	tablespoon fresh parsley, chopped fine
1	teaspoon olive oil
3	cups water
1/4	teaspoon sea salt
1/4	teaspoon black pepper, fresh ground

Heat a large non-stick skillet and sauté the onion and garlic in olive oil. Add the turnip and parsnip and continue to sauté for 5 minutes. Add the carrot and sauté for 3 minutes. Add the water and bring to a boil. Cover and simmer for 30 minutes or until cooked. Adjust the seasonings and serve hot, garnished with fresh parsley.

Notes: Excellent source of Vitamin C, A and Folacin. Good
source of Vitamin B6 and B1.

1/2 cup of nonfat sour cream may be added to the cooked soup to increase the calcium content of the soup.

Tomato Soup

12	medium tomatoes, peeled and chopped
1	large chopped onion
3	tablespoons tomato paste
3	cups chicken broth
1	teaspoon sugar
1/2	teaspoon black pepper, fresh ground
1/2	teaspoon Tabasco sauce
1/2	teaspoon salt
1	teaspoon fresh basil

Serving Size: 6
Prep Time: 0:30

Total Calories 105
Protein 8g
Carbohydrate 16g
Fat 2g
Cholesterol 1mg
Dietary Fiber 3g
% Calories from
Fat 17%

Combine the tomatoes, onion, chicken broth and tomato paste in a large saucepan. Bring to a boil, reduce the heat, cover and simmer for 15-20 minutes. Cool and blend until smooth. Return to the pan, add the seasonings and heat through. Serve garnished with finely chopped fresh tomato.

Notes: Excellent source of Vitamin C, A, Folacin and Niacin. Good source of Vitamin B6, B1, B2 and Iron.

Yogurt Soup with Mint

2 1/2	cups yogurt, skim milk
1 1/2	cups nonfat sour cream
2	cups vegetable broth
1/2	teaspoon roasted and ground cumin seed
1	teaspoon salt
2	teaspoons fresh lemon juice
1	tablespoon fresh chopped mint

Serving Size: 6
Prep Time: 0:10
Stand Time: 0:30+

Total Calories 129
Protein 9g
Carbohydrate 18g
Fat <1g
Cholesterol 7mg
Dietary Fiber 1g
% Calories from
Fat 7%

Beat the yogurt until light and creamy, add the sour cream, vegetable broth, ground cumin seed, salt, lemon juice and fresh mint. Adjust the seasoning and serve chilled.

Notes: Excellent source of Vitamin A, B12 and Calcium.
Good source of Vitamin B2, Folacin and Zinc.

Vegetables and Vegetarian Dishes

Serving Size: 4
Prep Time: 0:15

Total Calories 62
Protein 2g
Carbohydrate 13g
Fat <1g
Cholesterol 0mg
Dietary Fiber 4g
% Calories from
Fat 7%

Brussels Sprouts and Chestnuts

2   cups brussels sprouts
1/2   cup roasted chestnuts

Steam brussels sprouts until just tender (8-10 minutes). Place on a serving dish and arrange warmed roasted chestnuts on top. Serve with roast turkey or chicken.

Notes: Excellent source of Vitamin A, C and Folacin.
         Good source of Vitamin B6.

Eggplant Parmesan

3	medium eggplants, sliced 1/2" thick
1	chopped red bell pepper
1	tablespoon olive oil
1	clove crushed garlic
2	medium chopped onions
1	pound shredded carrots
1	pound mushrooms
1/2	small can black olives, sliced
15	ounces canned tomatoes
6	ounces tomato paste
1 1/2	teaspoons oregano
1	cup mozzarella cheese, part skim milk
1 1/2	cups Ricotta cheese, nonfat
1	tablespoon, Parmesan cheese
1	cup chopped parsley
1 1/2	cups bread crumbs
1	teaspoon black pepper

Serving Size: 8
Prep Time: 1:15

Total Calories 336
Protein 19g
Carbohydrate 48g
Fat 10g
Cholesterol 23mg
Dietary Fiber 10g
% Calories from
Fat 25%

Preheat the oven to 350°F. Sprinkle salt on the eggplant slices and set aside for 20 minutes. Heat the oil in non-stick skillet and sauté the onions and garlic for 3 minutes or until transparent. Add the mushrooms and heat for 2 minutes. Add the shredded carrots and red pepper and cook for 2 minutes more while stirring. Add the tomatoes, tomato paste, olives and oregano. Season to taste and set aside. Drain and wipe dry the eggplant slices. Lay them in a large oiled ovenproof dish and add a layer of mozzarella and ricotta cheese, then a layer of the vegetable mixture. Repeat once more and finally sprinkle with Parmesan cheese. Place in the oven and bake for 45 minutes.

Notes:　Excellent source of Vitamin C, A, B6, B1, B2, Folacin, Niacin, Calcium, Iron and Zinc.

Fennel Ratatouille

Serving Size: 4
Prep Time: 1:10

Total Calories 100
Protein 4g
Carbohydrate 19g
Fat 2g
Cholesterol 0mg
Dietary Fiber 3g
% Calories from
Fat 19%

2	fennel bulbs
1	pound red ripe tomatoes
2	medium sliced onions
2	sliced zucchini
2	tablespoons fresh chopped parsley
1/2	teaspoon fresh thyme
1/4	teaspoon salt
1/4	teaspoon fresh ground black pepper
1/2	tablespoon extra virgin olive oil

Heat the olive oil in a non-stick skillet and sauté the onions and garlic for 3-4 minutes until transparent. Add the fennel bulbs cut into slices, layered with zucchini and tomatoes. Sprinkle with herbs and season to taste. Cover the skillet and cook slowly for approximately an hour or until the fennel is tender. Serve hot or cold, garnished with chopped parsley.

Notes: Excellent source of Vitamin C, A and Folacin. Good source of Vitamin B6, B1, Niacin, Calcium and Iron.

French Peas

2	cups green peas
1/2	cup small white onions
1/2	teaspoon butter (optional)

Boil 1/2 cup of water and add green peas. Simmer for 5-8 minutes until cooked. Add onions and keep warm with pan covered. Add seasoning to taste. Add butter for optional shiny appearance.

Notes: Excellent source of Vitamin C and Folacin. Good source of Vitamin B1.

Serving Size: 4
Prep Time: 0:10

Total Calories 62
Protein 4g
Carbohydrate 11g
Fat <1g
Cholesterol 0mg
Dietary Fiber 4g
% Calories from
Fat 4%

Frittata with Spinach

Serving Size: 4
Prep Time: 1:00

Total Calories 134
Protein 12 g
Carbohydrate 5g
Fat 7 g
Cholesterol 114 mg
Dietary Fiber 3g
% Calories from
Fat 49%

2	eggs
2	egg whites
1/2	teaspoon salt
1	clove crushed garlic
1	teaspoon paprika
1/4	teaspoon red pepper flakes (optional)
1/2	tablespoon olive oil
1/2	cup grated Parmesan cheese
1	pound spinach leaves, chopped fine

Preheat the oven to 350°F. Place the washed spinach in a large saucepan and cook covered for 3-4 minutes, shaking frequently. Drain well. Beat the eggs together (or use 1 1/2 cups of liquid egg substitute) and add half of the eggs to the chopped spinach. Mix in 1/4 cup of the grated Parmesan. Prepare an 8" round ovenproof dish by lightly brushing with oil. Pour the egg and spinach mixture into the dish and sprinkle with the red pepper flakes. Pour the rest of the egg mixture over this and sprinkle with the rest of the Parmesan and paprika. Bake for 45 minutes and serve hot with a green salad as a main dish.

Notes: Excellent source of Vitamin C, A, B2, Folacin, Calcium and Iron. Good source of Zinc.

Garlic Mashed Potatoes

4	peeled potatoes
1/2	cup skim milk
3	cloves crushed garlic
1	teaspoon butter
1/4	teaspoon sea salt
1/4	teaspoon black pepper, fresh ground

Serving Size: 4
Prep Time: 0:30

Total Calories 111
Protein 4g
Carbohydrate 23g
Fat 1g
Cholesterol 3mg
Dietary Fiber 2g
% Calories from
Fat 9%

Heat the oven to 425°F. Wrap the garlic cloves in aluminum foil and bake for 20 minutes. Unwrap and cool. Slice the potatoes evenly and place in a saucepan. Cover with cold water and bring to a boil. Simmer for 5-8 minutes until soft. Drain and mash until smooth. Cut the base from the garlic cloves and squeeze pulp into mashed potatoes. Warm milk and add to potatoes with butter and seasonings. Serve hot or cold.

Notes: Excellent source of Vitamin C. Good source of Vitamin B6 and Niacin.

Glazed Carrots

5	medium carrots
1/2	tablespoon butter
1/2	tablespoon fresh lemon juice
1	tablespoon fresh parsley, finely chopped

Serving Size: 4
Prep Time: 0:30

Total Calories 52
Protein 1g
Carbohydrate 10g
Fat 1g
Cholesterol 4mg
Dietary Fiber 3g
% Calories from
Fat 17%

Peel and julienne carrots into 1/4" strips. Place them in a medium saucepan and cover with cold water. Bring to a boil and boil gently for 10-12 minutes or until tender. Drain and set aside in a warm place. In the same pan, melt butter and add lemon juice. Add carrots and toss for 1-2 minutes until well glazed. Serve hot, garnished with fresh chopped parsley.

Notes: Excellent source of Vitamin A. Good source of Vitamin C.

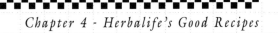

Leeks á la Grécque

4	medium leeks
1	tablespoon olive oil
1	cup water
1	tablespoon tomato paste
1	teaspoon sugar
1/2	cup rice
12	small black olives
1	tablespoon parsley
1	teaspoon lemon juice
3	slices lemon

Serving Size: 4
Prep Time: 0:30

Total Calories 229
Protein 5g
Carbohydrate 48
Fat 5g
Cholesterol 0mg
Dietary Fiber 3g
% Calories from
Fat 19%

Wash and slice leeks into 1 1/2" pieces. Steam for 5-6 minutes until cooked. Cool. Boil water, oil, tomato paste and sugar in a large pan and simmer for 5 minutes. Add rice, cover the pot and simmer for 8 minutes or until the liquid is completely absorbed by the rice. Turn off the heat and leave the pan covered for 10 minutes. Add lemon juice and arrange with leeks on a serving dish. Garnish with olives, parsley and lemon slices.

Notes: Excellent source of Vitamin C, B6, B1, Folacin and Iron. Good source of Niacin and Calcium.

Potatoes au Gratin

2	pounds peeled potatoes
2	cups skim milk
4	tablespoons low-fat Swiss cheese, grated
2	tablespoons Parmesan cheese, grated
1/4	teaspoon salt
1/4	teaspoon white pepper

Serving Size: 4
Prep Time: 0:30

Total Calories 111
Protein 8g
Carbohydrate 17g
Fat 1g
Cholesterol 7mg
Dietary Fiber <1g
% Calories from
Fat 11%

Place the sliced potatoes in cold water and leave for 5 minutes. Drain and place in an ovenproof gratin dish. Add milk and season to taste with salt and pepper. Cover with foil and place in a medium hot oven (325°F) for 20 minutes. Add cheese and return to the oven for 20-30 minutes or until the potatoes are cooked through. Serve hot.

Notes: Excellent source of Vitamin C, B12 and Calcium.
Good source of Vitamin B6 and B2.

Sautéed Spinach

2	pounds fresh washed spinach
I	clove crushed garlic
I	tablespoon sesame oil
1/4	teaspoon salt
1/4	teaspoon black pepper, fresh ground

Serving Size: 4
Prep Time: 0:10

Place the washed spinach in a large saucepan and cook covered for 3-4 minutes, shaking frequently. Drain well. Heat the sesame oil in a large skillet and add the crushed garlic. Quickly stir-fry the spinach in the garlic and sesame oil and serve hot.

Notes: Excellent source of Vitamin A and Folacin. Good source of Vitamin C.

This dish is so low in calories that the % fat calories seems high.

Total Calories 38
Protein <1g
Carbohydrate 1g
Fat 3g
Cholesterol 0mg
Dietary Fiber 1g
% Calories from
Fat 71%

Spinach, Brown Rice and Tofu

I	cup brown rice
2/3	pounds tofu, firm
2	pounds spinach leaves
I	tablespoon soy sauce
I	tablespoon olive oil
I	tablespoon sesame seeds

Serving Size: 8
Prep Time: 0:45

Total Calories 164
Protein 10g
Carbohydrate 22g
Fat 4g
Cholesterol 0mg
Dietary Fiber 4g
% Calories from
Fat 23%

Cook brown rice by covering in cold water with about 1/2 inch extra water on top. Bring to a boil and boil for a minute. Cover, turn the heat down and simmer for 30 - 40 minutes. Check the moisture level twice during cooking and adjust if necessary. Toast the sesame seeds for a few minutes in a medium oven (350°F). Wash and cook spinach in water by shaking a covered pot over a medium heat for 3-5 minutes. Arrange tofu in the middle of an ovenproof dish with spinach around the outside. Moisten with soy sauce and sprinkle the sesame seeds. Warm through in 325°F oven and serve with rice.

Notes: Excellent source of Vitamin C, A, B6, Folacin and Iron. Good source of Vitamin B1, B2, Niacin, Calcium and Zinc.

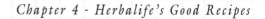

Sweet and Sour Vegetables

2	cups sliced carrots
2	cups chopped bok choy
2	cups chopped green bell pepper
3	cups chopped tomatoes
1	cup chopped onions
2	tablespoons tomato paste
1/4	cup soy sauce
1/3	cup pineapple juice
1	small can sliced water chestnuts
1	tablespoon corn starch

Serving Size: 6
Prep Time: 0:45

Total Calories 76
Protein 3g
Carbohydrate 17g
Fat <1g
Cholesterol 0mg
Dietary Fiber 4g
% Calories from
Fat 6%

Steam the carrots till tender, add the bok choy and green peppers. Set aside. Dissolve the corn starch in the pineapple juice. Place the soy sauce, water and tomato paste in a small pan. Add the corn starch and pineapple mixture and bring to the boil. Stir well until it thickens. Sauté the onions in a covered, heavy-bottomed pan. Add the water chestnuts and the other vegetables and warm through. Add the sauce and serve in a dish with rice or pasta as a main dish.

Notes: Excellent source of Vitamin C, A, B6 and Niacin.
Good source of Vitamin B1 and Niacin.

Sweet Potatoes with Almonds

2	pounds sweet potatoes
1	tablespoon slivered almonds

Serving Size: 4
Prep Time: 0:30

Total Calories 82
Protein 2g
Carbohydrate 16g
Fat <1g
Cholesterol 0mg
Dietary Fiber 2g
% Calories from
Fat 15%

Preheat the oven to 400 °F. Toast the slivered almonds for 3-4 minutes until brown. Remove and set aside to cool. Bake the sweet potatoes for 20-30 minutes until soft. (They can also be baked in the microwave oven). When cool, split open and scoop out the center. Mash, adding a little water if necessary. Spread in a serving dish and cover with toasted slivered almonds.

Notes: Excellent source of Vitamin C and A. Good source of Vitamin B6.

Vegetable Curry

4	cups brown rice
1 1/2	cups cauliflower florets
2	medium carrots, sliced thin
1	cup broccoli florets
1	medium red bell pepper, deseeded and sliced
1	medium onion, sliced thin
1	cup frozen green peas
15	ounces canned tomatoes
1	tablespoon toasted bread crumbs

SAUCE

2	tablespoons olive oil
1	tablespoon curry powder
2	cloves garlic
1/4	teaspoon red chili pepper or cayenne
1/2	cup vegetable broth
2	tablespoons fresh lime juice

Serving Size: 8
Prep Time: 0:30

Total Calories 434
Protein 11g
Carbohydrate 86g
Fat 7g
Cholesterol 0mg
Dietary Fiber 4g
% Calories from
Fat 13%

Cook rice by covering with extra 1/2 " water on top. Bring to a boil and boil for a minute uncovered. Cover the pot and simmer gently for 30 minutes. Check water level and adjust so that all water is absorbed and the rice is moist when cooked. Steam the cauliflower, sliced carrots and broccoli for 7-8 minutes, then add the red bell pepper, sliced onion and green peas and steam 3 minutes more. Add the tomatoes at the last minute and mix. Set aside in a casserole dish. Heat oil in a non-stick pan and add curry powder, garlic and red chili pepper. Saute for 2-3 minutes. Add vegetable broth and boil for 3 minutes. Stir in fresh lime juice and pour over the vegetables. Sprinkle the top with toasted bread crumbs and serve hot.

Notes: Excellent source of Vitamin A, B6, B1, Folacin, Niacin and Zinc. Good source of Vitamin B2 and Iron. Curry powder varies in intensity according to the brand. Start with a small amount and add extra to taste. The flavor will intensify as the dish stands.

Vegetarian Stew

Serving Size: 8
Prep Time: 0:45

Total Calories 210
Protein 8g
Carbohydrate 41g
Fat 3g
Cholesterol 0mg
Dietary Fiber 5g
% Calories from
Fat 12%

1	cup cooked brown rice
3/4	cup bulgur
2/3	cup cooked soybeans
1/2	pound sliced string beans
1	teaspoon chili powder
1/2	teaspoon hot sauce
16	ounces canned tomatoes
12	ounces canned corn, drained
1	teaspoon olive oil
1	small can green chilis, drained
1/2	teaspoon black pepper, fresh ground

Soak the soybeans overnight and discard the water. Cook the brown rice by covering with cold water and bringing to a boil. Reduce heat, cover pot and simmer for 30 minutes or until tender. Cook the bulgur wheat in a similar manner in a separate pot. Drain the cans of chilis and corn. Heat the olive oil and add rice, bulgur, and soybeans. Quickly sauté until well mixed. Add string beans, corn, tomatoes and chilis. Season with chili powder and hot sauce. Add pepper. Simmer for 15 minutes. Serve hot.

Notes: Excellent source of Vitamin C and Folacin. Good source of Vitamin A, B6, B1, B2, Niacin and Iron.

Vegetarian Tofu

1 1/2	pounds low-fat tofu, firm
1/2	tablespoon olive oil
2	cloves crushed garlic
2	medium chopped onions
1	cup sliced mushrooms
1/3	cup Tamari soy sauce
1	teaspoon fresh chopped basil
1/2	teaspoon thyme
1/4	teaspoon marjoram
1/4	teaspoon savory
dash	Tabasco sauce
2	cups vegetable broth
2	cups cooked rice

Serving Size: 6
Prep Time: 0:45

Total Calories 231
Protein 12g
Carbohydrate 33g
Fat 6g
Cholesterol 1mg
Dietary Fiber 3g
% Calories from
Fat 23%

Heat the olive oil in a non-stick skillet. Add the garlic and onions and sauté for 3-5 minutes until transparent. Add the mushrooms and cook 2 more minutes, shaking the skillet constantly. Remove the vegetables and set aside on a warm dish. Cut the tofu into 1-1 1/2" size cubes. In a mixing bowl combine the Tamari, basil, thyme, savory, marjoram and Tabasco. Dip the tofu cubes in the mixture and brown the cubes in the skillet. Add the vegetable broth to the skillet and return the vegetable mixture. Simmer for 10 minutes and serve hot with rice as a main dish.

Notes: Excellent source of Vitamin A and Iron. Good source of Vitamin B6, B1, B2, Folacin, Niacin, Calcium and Zinc.

MEASURES

Weight or Mass

1 ounce (oz)	=	28 grams
1 pound (lb) or 16 oz	=	450 grams
1 gram (g)	=	0.035 oz
1 kilogram (kg)	=	2.2 lbs (35 oz)

VOLUME

1 teaspoon (t)	=	5 milliliters (ml)
1 tablespoon (T)	=	3 t or 15 ml
2 T	=	⅛ Cup (C)
12 T	=	¾ C
1 C	=	8 fluid ounces (fl oz)
1 fl oz	=	30 ml or 2 T
8 fl oz	=	½ pint or 250 ml
1 pint (pt)	=	2 C or 16 fl oz or 500 ml
1 quart	=	4 C or 32 fl oz or 1 liter
1 gallon	=	16 C or 128 fl oz or 4 liters or 4 quarts
1 Liter	=	1.06 quarts

YIELDS

1 lb dry beans	yields	2 C dry beans
2 C dry beans	yields	5-6 C cooked beans
2 oz dry spaghetti	yields	1 C cooked spaghetti
3 oz fresh pasta	yields	1 C cooked fresh pasta

COMMON EQUIVALENT MEASURES

1/4 C sugar	=	1 ¾ oz
1 C sugar	=	7 oz
1 T butter	=	½ oz
1 oz butter	=	2 T
1 stick butter	=	½ C or 8 T or 4 oz
1 C butter	=	16 T or 2 sticks or 8 oz
1 oz flour	=	¼ C
1 C flour	=	5 oz
1 t baking powder	=	¼ t baking soda + ½ t cream of tartar
1 clove garlic	=	⅛ t garlic powder
1 t salt	=	2400 mg sodium
1 t dried herbs	=	3 t fresh herbs

TEMPERATURES

	Fahrenheit	Centigrade
Freezer temperature	0	-18
Body heat	98.6	37
Water simmers	180	82
Water boils	212	100
Low oven	250	120
Moderate oven	350	175
Hot	425	220
Very hot	500	260

TO CONVERT

°F	=	$\frac{9}{5}(°C) + 32$
°C	=	$\frac{5}{9}(°F) - 32$

Notes

Nutrients listed as "Excellent" source indicates 20% or more of the RDA. "Good" source indicates between 10-19% of RDA.

The values for the following nutrients are listed:

	10% RDA	**20% RDA**
Vitamin A	8 RE	16 RE
Vitamin C	6 mg	12 mg
Vitamin B6	0.17 mg	0.34 mg
Vitamin B12	0.2 mcg	0.4 mcg
Vitamin B1	0.11 mg	o.22 mg
Vitamin B2	0.13 mg	0.26 mg
Folacin	17.5 mcg	35 mcg
Niacin	1.7 mg	3.5 mg
Calcium	80 mg	160 mg
Iron	1.5 mg	3 mg
Zinc	1.2 mg	2.4 mg

All the recipes have been designed for a balanced diet to provide between 20 and 25% of the calories from fat. Wherever possible olive oil or canola oil is chosen over butter or lard because of its healthier fatty acid profile (see Chapter One).

Recipe Index